10.

R.F. Cheeney
February 1970

TITLES IN THE POPULAR LECTURES IN MATHEMATICS SERIES

POPULAR LECTURES IN MATHEMATICS

Editors: I. N. SNEDDON *and* M. STARK

VOLUME 13

SHORTEST PATHS
Variational Problems

SHORTEST PATHS
Variational Problems

BY

L. A. LYUSTERNIK

TRANSLATED AND ADAPTED FROM THE RUSSIAN BY

P. COLLINS AND **ROBERT B. BROWN**

SURVEY OF
RECENT EAST EUROPEAN MATHEMATICAL LITERATURE

A project conducted by
ALFRED L. PUTNAM and **IZAAK WIRSZUP**

Department of Mathematics,
The University of Chicago, under a
grant from the National Science Foundation

PERGAMON PRESS
OXFORD · LONDON · EDINBURGH · NEW YORK
PARIS · FRANKFURT

1964

PERGAMON PRESS LTD.
Headington Hill Hall, Oxford
4 & 5 Fitzroy Square, London W.1

PERGAMON PRESS (SCOTLAND) LTD.
2 & 3 Teviot Place, Edinburgh 1

PERGAMON PRESS INC.
122 East 55th Street, New York 22, N.Y.

GAUTHIER-VILLARS ED.
55 Quai des Grands-Augustins, Paris 6

PERGAMON PRESS G.m.b.H.
Kaiserstrasse 75, Frankfurt am Main

Distributed in the Western Hemisphere by
THE MACMILLAN COMPANY · NEW YORK
pursuant to a special arrangement with
Pergamon Press Ltd.

This book is an edited translation of *Kratchaischie linii*,
Moscow, 1955.

Library of Congress Catalog Card No. 64–14145

*Set in 10 on 11 pt. Times N.R. and printed in Great Britain
at the* PITMAN PRESS, BATH

CONTENTS

PART II

INTRODUCTION

In this booklet we investigate from an elementary point of view a number of so-called variational problems. In these problems we examine functions which assign a certain number† to each curve in a family of curves on a surface. Among all such curves we then seek the one whose assigned number is the greatest or least. Consider, for example, the following problem: from among all the curves on a surface which join two given points, find the shortest. Here the family consists of all the curves joining the two points, and the number assigned to each curve is its length. Consider also the following problem: from among all closed plane curves of a given length, find the one that encloses the greatest area. Here the family consists of all the plane curves of the given length, and the number assigned to each curve is the area it encloses.

The material of the booklet was, in the main, presented by the author in lectures to the secondary school mathematics circle at the Moscow State University. The first part (Sections 1–10) deals with essentially the same material as the author's booklet *Geodesic Lines*, written in 1940.

This booklet presupposes only a knowledge of high school mathematics. The first chapter is entirely elementary; the others, although they do not demand special knowledge, do demand somewhat greater skill in reading mathematics and thinking clearly in terms of mathematical concepts.

The entire booklet can be considered as an elementary introduction to the calculus of variations—that branch of mathematics which studies the problem of determining maxima and minima of functionals. The calculus of variations is seldom discussed in the first intensive course in higher mathematics offered, say, in technical colleges. However, we believe that a student about to undertake the study of higher mathematics can profit from some additional reading.

† Such a "function" is called a functional.

The reader who is acquainted with the elements of mathematical analysis should have no difficulty supplying thoroughly rigorous definitions and proofs in those places where we have fallen short of complete rigor. (He will often find explanations in small print indicating how this may be done.) For example, instead of speaking of infinitesimal numbers and their approximate equality, we should speak of equality of limits. If the more exacting reader is not satisfied with the level of rigor and logical finish of the treatment presented here, this may serve as evidence for him of the necessity for that logical refinement of basic concepts encountered, for example, in university courses in mathematical analysis. Without such refinement a strict and systematic presentation of parts of analysis such as the calculus of variations is impossible.

Mathematical analysis has developed a powerful analytical apparatus which sometimes solves many different problems automatically. However, at all stages of his study of mathematics, it is important for the student to appreciate the simple geometric and physical ideas behind the problem being solved. He must be able to solve problems, so to speak, by the look of them: to give proofs which, though not entirely rigorous, are simple and perspicuous.

If this booklet in some measure assists the reader in the development of these elements of mathematical maturity, then the author will consider that the labor spent in writing it has not been wasted.

1

SHORTEST PATHS ON SIMPLE SURFACES

1. Shortest Paths on Polyhedral Surfaces

1. Shortest paths on a dihedral angle. The reader certainly knows that a straight line segment is the shortest of all paths connecting two points on a plane.

Let us now consider two points A and B on some arbitrary surface. These two points can be joined by infinitely many different paths lying on the surface. Which of these paths is the shortest? In other words, how should we move on the surface so that we take the shortest route from point A to point B?

We shall solve this problem first of all for some simple surfaces. Let us begin with the following problem. We are given a dihedral

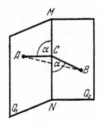

Fig. 1

angle† with faces Q_1 and Q_2 and the edge MN. On the faces of the angle we are given two points: point A on Q_1 and point B on Q_2 (Fig. 1). The points A and B can be joined by infinitely many different paths lying on the faces Q_1 and Q_2 of the dihedral angle. Find the shortest of these paths.

† A dihedral angle is the surface formed by two intersecting planes. In Fig. 1 only a *part* of an infinite dihedral angle is shown.

If the dihedral angle is a straight angle (180°), then the faces Q_1 and Q_2 are continuations of one another (that is, they form a single plane), and the required shortest path is the straight line segment AB joining the points A and B. If the dihedral angle is not a straight angle, then the faces Q_1 and Q_2 do not form a single plane, and the line segment AB does not lie on these faces. Let us rotate one of the faces about the line MN until each face is a continuation of the other; in other words, let us develop the dihedral angle into a plane (Fig. 2). The faces Q_1 and Q_2 become the half-planes Q_1' and Q_2'. The straight line MN becomes the straight line $M'N'$ which separates Q_1' from Q_2'; the points A and B become points A' and B' (A' is situated on Q_1', B' on Q_2'); every path lying on the faces of the dihedral angle and joining the points A and B becomes a path

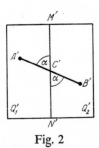

Fig. 2

of the same length joining the points A' and B' in the plane. The shortest path joining the points A and B on the faces of the dihedral angle becomes the shortest path joining the points A' and B' in the plane, that is, the straight line segment $A'B'$. This segment intersects the straight line $M'N'$ at some point C'; the angles $A'C'M'$ and $N'C'B'$ are equal, because they are vertical angles (Fig. 2). We shall denote the value of each of these angles by α.

Let us now rotate Q_1' and Q_2' around $M'N'$ so that the original dihedral angle is restored. The half-planes Q_1' and Q_2' are turned back into the faces Q_1 and Q_2 of the dihedral angle, $M'N'$ into the edge MN, and points A' and B' into the points A (on face Q_1) and B (on face Q_2); the straight line segment $A'B'$ becomes the shortest path lying on the faces of the dihedral angle and joining the points A and B. Obviously, this shortest path is the broken line ACB whose segments AC and CB lie on faces Q_1 and Q_2 (Fig. 1). It is also obvious that the angles ACM and NCB into which the equal angles $A'C'M'$ and $N'C'B'$ have been transformed are also equal to

α; therefore these angles are equal. Thus *the shortest of the paths on the surface of a dihedral angle which join two points A and B that lie on different faces is the broken line ACB, where C is the point on the edge MN of the dihedral angle for which angles ACM and NCB are equal.*

The problem that has just been considered is sometimes presented in the following amusing form: A fly is sitting on a point A of one wall of a rectangular room; how should it move along the walls in order to take the shortest route from A to a point B lying on an adjoining wall? It is not difficult to find the solution now.

2. Shortest paths on a many-sided surface. Let us now consider a somewhat more complicated problem. We are given a many-sided surface (Fig. 3) with faces Q_1, Q_2, Q_3, . . ., Q_n and edges M_1N_1, M_2N_2, M_3N_3, . . ., $M_{n-1}N_{n-1}$ (see Fig. 3; here $n = 4$). On two

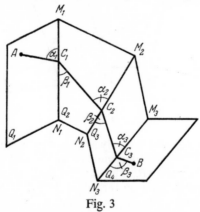

Fig. 3

different faces of this many-sided surface (for example, Q_1 and Q_4) we are given points A and B. Find the shortest path joining A and B and lying on the surface.

Let AB denote the shortest path and suppose that it passes over the surfaces Q_1, Q_2, Q_3, Q_4. We develop the part of the surface consisting of these faces into a plane (Fig. 4). Then the faces become polygons Q_1', Q_2', Q_3', Q_4' lying in this plane, and the corresponding edges M_1N_1, M_2N_2, M_3N_3 along which the faces Q_1, Q_2, Q_3, Q_4 adjoin one another become the sides $M_1'N_1'$, $M_2'N_2'$, $M_3'N_3'$ of the polygons Q_1', Q_2', Q_3', Q_4' along which the latter adjoin one another. The points A and B become points A' and B' of the plane, and the paths joining A and B on the surface change into paths joining A' and B' in the plane. The shortest path joining A and B becomes the shortest plane path connecting A' and B', that is, the straight line segment $A'B'$. The previous argument can be repeated here in its entirety; the vertical angles α_1 and β_1 that are formed by the straight line $A'B'$ with the edge $M_1'N_1'$ are equal; in exactly the same way, the pairs of vertical angles α_2 and β_2, α_3 and β_3 formed by the straight line $A'B'$ with the edges $M_2'N_2'$, $M_3'N_3'$ (Fig. 4) are equal.

If we now fold the part of the plane that is formed by the polygons into the many-sided surface so that the polygon Q_1' is transformed back into the face Q_1, the polygon Q_2' into the face Q_2, the polygon

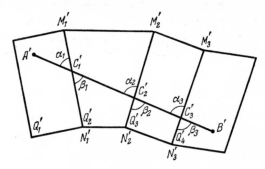

Fig. 4

Q_3' into the face Q_3, and the polygon Q_4' into the face Q_4, then the points A' and B' become the points A and B, and the line segment $A'B'$ becomes the path AB. The shortest path AB will be a broken line with its vertices lying on the edges M_1N_1, M_2N_2, M_3N_3 of the many-sided surface. The angles α_1 and β_1 (and also α_2 and β_2, α_3 and β_3) that are formed by two adjacent segments of the broken line and an edge of the surface will be equal.

3. Shortest paths on the lateral surface of a prism. In Fig. 5 is shown a prism† and the shortest of all the paths on its surface which join two points A and B situated on different lateral faces of the prism. This shortest path is a broken line with vertices C_1, C_2, C_3, . . ., on the edges of the prism. The angles which any two adjacent segments of this path make with the edge of the prism on which

† The lateral faces of the prism must be considered to be indefinitely extended.

their common vertex lies, are equal, by virtue of the previous argument:

$$\alpha_1 = \beta_1, \quad \alpha_2 = \beta_2, \quad \alpha_3 = \beta_3, \ldots$$

But, in addition, we have $\beta_1 = \alpha_2$. For these angles are alternate interior angles formed by the parallel lines M_1N_1 and M_2N_2 and the transversal C_1C_2. In exactly the same way, $\beta_2 = \alpha_3$. Thus, we have

$$\alpha_1 = \beta_1 = \alpha_2 = \beta_2 = \alpha_3 = \beta_3 = \ldots$$

In other words, *every segment of the shortest broken line joining two points A and B on the surface of a prism, makes the same angle with the edges of the prism which it meets.*

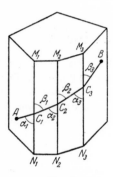

Fig. 5

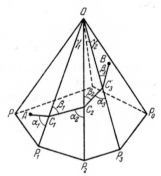

Fig. 6

4. Shortest paths on the surface of a pyramid. Let A and B be two points on lateral faces of a pyramid† with the vertex O (Fig. 6). These points can be joined by infinitely many paths lying on the surface of the pyramid, among which there will be a shortest AB. On the basis of the previous argument, the path AB is the broken line having vertices $C_1, C_2, C_3, \ldots$, on the edges of the pyramid such that the angles α_1 and β_1, α_2 and β_2, α_3 and $\beta_3, \ldots$, which are formed by the segments of this broken line and the edges of the pyramid are pairwise equal:

$$\alpha_1 = \beta_1, \quad \alpha_2 = \beta_2, \quad \alpha_3 = \beta_3, \ldots$$

† The lateral faces of the pyramid are considered to be indefinitely extended.

5

Let us examine the face P_1OP_2 on which the segment C_1C_2 lies. If γ_1 denotes the angle P_1OP_2, then in the triangle C_1OC_2 the angle α_2 is an external angle, and the angles β_1 and γ_1 are the opposite interior angles. An external angle of a triangle is equal to the sum of the opposite interior angles, and, consequently,

$$\alpha_2 = \beta_1 + \gamma_1 \quad \text{or} \quad \alpha_2 - \beta_1 = \gamma_1.$$

But since $\beta_1 = \alpha_1$, we have $\alpha_2 - \alpha_1 = \gamma_1$. Similarly, $\alpha_3 - \alpha_2 = \gamma_2$, where γ_2 is the angle formed by the adjacent lateral edges OP_2 and OP_3 at the vertex O, and so on.

Thus *the difference between the angles in which the shortest path intersects any pair of edges of a pyramid is equal to the sum of the angles at the vertices of all the faces of the pyramid between these two edges.*

2. Shortest Paths on Cylindrical Surfaces

1. Shortest paths on the surface of a cylinder. We consider now the problem of finding shortest paths on some simple curved surfaces. We shall begin with the surface of a right circular cylinder.†

Consider a circle C. The surface generated by a straight line that intersects C and is perpendicular to the plane of C is called a

Fig. 7

cylindrical surface. The straight line passing through the center of C and perpendicular to the plane of C is called the *axis* of the cylinder. The lines forming the surface of the cylinder are called the *generators* of the cylindrical surface.

Suppose we are given two points A and B on the surface of a cylinder (Fig. 7). Among all the curves that join A and B and that lie on the surface of the cylinder, we seek the one which is shortest.

† The lateral surface of the *finite* cylinder which we consider here (Fig. 7) is part of an infinite cylindrical surface.

Let us denote this shortest curve joining points A and B by $\overset{\frown}{AB}$.
First we shall consider the case in which A and B do not lie on the
same generator.

Let us cut the lateral surface of the cylinder along some generator
PQ (not intersecting $\overset{\frown}{AB}$) and unroll the cylinder onto a plane; we
obtain a rectangle (Fig. 8). (One pair of sides of the rectangle,
$P'P''$ and $Q'Q''$, was obtained by unrolling the circles which form
the boundaries of the surface of the cylinder; the other pair, $P'Q'$
and $P''Q''$, was obtained from the two edges of the cut PQ.) The
generators of the cylinder become straight lines parallel to the side
$P'Q'$ of the rectangle. The points A and B become points A' and B'
lying inside the rectangle. The curves that join the points A and B

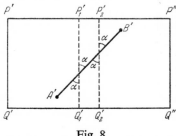

Fig. 8

on the cylinder become plane paths which join the points A' and
B' inside the rectangle. The arc $\overset{\frown}{AB}$—the shortest of the curves on
the cylinder which join the points A and B—becomes the shortest
of the plane paths which join the points A' and B', that is, the straight
line segment $A'B'$. Thus *upon developing the lateral surface of the
cylinder into a plane rectangle, the shortest curve $\overset{\frown}{AB}$ on the surface
of the cylinder becomes the straight line segment $A'B'$*. The generators of the cylinder P_1Q_1, P_2Q_2, . . ., become the straight lines
$P_1'Q_1'$, $P_2'Q_2'$, . . ., parallel to the sides $P'Q'$, $P''Q''$ of the rectangle
$P'Q'Q''P''$. The angles formed by the segment $A'B'$ with these
straight lines are equal, since they are corresponding angles made by
a transversal which cuts a series of parallel lines. Let us denote the
value of each of these angles by α.

We now roll up the rectangle $P'Q'Q''P''$ (pasting its opposite sides
$P'Q'$ and $P''Q''$ together) so that it again assumes the shape of the
cylinder. The points A' and B' become the points A and B of the
cylinder, and the straight line segment $A'B'$ becomes the shortest

curve *AB* on the surface of the cylinder. Since the straight line *A'B'* cuts all the straight lines parallel to *P'Q'* at the same angle α, *the shortest curve $\overparen{AB}$, into which A'B' is transformed, cuts all generators of the cylinder in the same angle* α (Fig. 7).

Let us consider the special case in which the points *A* and *B* lie on the same generator (Fig. 9). It is obvious that in this case *the segment AB of the generator will be the shortest path between the points A and B on the surface of the cylinder.*

In case the points *A* and *B* lie on the same right section of the cylinder (Fig. 10), *the arc $\overparen{AB}$ of this section is perpendicular to all the generators and is the shortest path which joins the points A and B.*

Fig. 9   Fig. 10

If the cylinder is cut along a generator not intersecting the curve $\overparen{AB}$ and developed into a plane rectangle, then in both the cases under consideration the shortest path becomes a segment parallel to a side of the rectangle. In all other cases, the shortest path cuts the generators at an angle which is not a right angle (and is not equal to zero).†

2. Helices. A curve on a cylindrical surface that intersects all generators in the same angle α ($\neq 90°$) is called a *helix*. A curve that intersects all generators in a right angle is simply a circle. Thus, a circle can be thought of as a limiting case of a helix (a helix for which α = 90°). Similarly, a generator of the cylinder is the other limiting case of a helix (a helix for which $\beta = 0°$).

Consider a point that moves on the surface of a cylinder. If the path of motion of the point is along a generator, then we shall

† It is interesting to compare the problem of finding the shortest curve on the surface of a cylinder with the problem of finding the shortest broken line on the surface of a prism, as considered above in subsection 3 of Section 1 (for which our problem is a limiting case).

speak of a *vertical* motion of the point, and we shall say that the motion is *positive* vertical motion if the point moves upward, *negative* if it moves downward. The motion of a point which moves around the cylinder along a circular path is called *rotation*; we shall call rotations in a counterclockwise direction *positive*, rotations in a clockwise direction *negative*.

Now let a point on a cylindrical surface be acted upon by two forces, one tending to move the point around the cylinder in a circle, the other tending to move it vertically along a generator. The result will be that the point moves along a curved path that winds around the cylinder. As a matter of fact, this path will be a helix on the

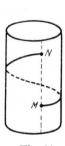

Fig. 11

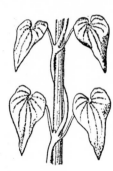

Fig. 12

surface of the cylinder. A helix is called a *right* helix if it is generated by a point traveling with a positive vertical motion combined with positive rotation (Fig. 11), and a *left* helix if the generating point travels with a positive vertical motion combined with negative rotation.

Most climbing plants (bindweed, kidney bean) curling around vertical supports take the form of right helices (Fig. 12). On the other hand, hops, for example, take the form of a left helix (Fig. 13).

Suppose a point moving along a helix meets a generator in a point M. As the point continues to move along the helix it intersects the same generator in another point N; when the point has traveled through the arc $\overarc{MN}$ of the helix, it will have completed a full revolution around the axis of the cylinder; at the same time it will have traveled upward a distance equal to the length of the segment MN (Fig. 11). If the speed of rotation is zero and the point is displaced

9

only parallel to the axis of the cylinder along a generator, then the first limiting case is obtained; the second limiting case is obtained when the speed of displacement parallel to the axis of the cylinder is zero and the point simply revolves in a circle around the axis.

On the basis of what has been said above, we can assert the following theorem:

Fig. 13

THEOREM. *The shortest path $\widehat{AB}$ joining two given points A and B on the surface of a cylinder is an arc of a helix.*

3. Helical arcs joining two given points. Two points on the surface of a cylinder can be joined by different helical arcs. In fact, let two points on the surface of a cylinder be joined by the shortest possible path $\widehat{AB}$; this path is an arc of a helix, and when the surface of the cylinder is unrolled (cut along a generator not intersecting the path $\widehat{AB}$) into a plane rectangle, it becomes a straight line segment (Figs. 7 and 8).

Let us now cut the cylinder along the generator P_1Q_1 which intersects the shortest path $\widehat{AB}$ at point C (Fig. 7). The path $\widehat{AB}$ is divided into two parts, $\widehat{AC}$ and $\widehat{CB}$; if the surface of the cylinder is unrolled into a plane rectangle, then the points A and B become

10

points A'' and B'' of the rectangle (Fig. 14: we imagine $\overset{\frown}{AB}$ drawn on the *inside* surface of the cylinder), and the parts $\overset{\frown}{AC}$ and $\overset{\frown}{CB}$ of the path $\overset{\frown}{AB}$ become the corresponding line segments $A''C''$ and $B''C'$. But the points A'' and B'' can be joined by the straight line segment $A''B''$, which lies inside the rectangle $P_1'Q_1'Q_1''P_1''$. Obviously $A''B''$ is shorter than any other path *lying inside this rectangle* and joining the points A'' and B''.

Let us roll up our rectangle into a cylinder once more, pasting together the lateral sides $P_1'Q_1'$ and $P_1''Q_1''$ so that point C' coincides with point C'' and occupies the position C; then the points A'' and B'' again become points A and B on the surface of the cylinder, and

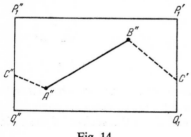

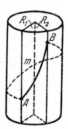

Fig. 14   Fig. 15

the segments $A''C''$ and $B''C'$ become the path $\overset{\frown}{AB}$, which is the shortest of all the paths on the surface of the cylinder which join points A and B. The segment $A''B''$ becomes the helical arc $\underset{\frown}{AB}$ which joins the same points A and B. In Fig. 15 $\overset{\frown}{AB}$ is an arc of a right helix and $\underset{\frown}{AB}$ of a left helix, both of which pass through the points A and B.

After the rectangle has been rolled into a cylinder, those lines which did not cut the sides of the rectangle become paths which do not cut the generator P_1Q_1 (because the edges of our rectangle $P_1'Q_1'$ and $P_1''Q_1''$ are pasted together along this line). Among these paths, the shortest will be the path AB = helical arc $\overset{\frown}{AmB}$ (Fig. 15). But it may not be the shortest of *all* paths on the surface of the cylinder which join the points A and B, because $\underset{\frown}{AB}$ is one such path, and may be shorter than AB.

Consider the half-plane R_1 determined by the point A and the axis of the cylinder, and the half-plane R_2 determined by the point B and the axis of the cylinder (Fig. 15).

11

These half-planes form two dihedral angles. The path $\overset{\frown}{AB}$ is included in one of them, and the path $\underset{\frown}{AB}$ in the other. Of these two paths, the shorter is the one that lies inside the smaller dihedral angle. If the dihedral angles are equal (that is, the half-planes R_1

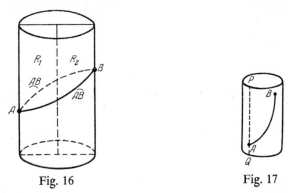

Fig. 16   Fig. 17

and R_2 are continuations of each other), then the arcs $\overset{\frown}{AB}$ and $\underset{\frown}{AB}$ are equal in length. In this case there are two shortest paths (of equal length) joining the points A and B on the surface of the cylinder (Fig. 16).

The two helical arcs $\overset{\frown}{AB}$ and $\underset{\frown}{AB}$ have a property in common: moving along either one of them from point A to point B we do not complete a full rotation around the axis of the cylinder.

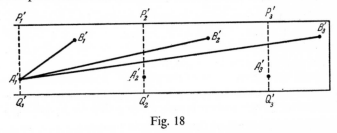

Fig. 18

Let us now wrap a long rectangular sheet of paper around the cylinder a number of times (we assume that its width is equal to the height of the cylinder) (Fig. 17). We stick a needle through this sheet at each of the points A and B, then we unroll the sheet into a plane rectangle. As a result of sticking the needle through the sheet at point A we shall have several puncture marks; in Fig. 18 these points are labeled A_1', A_2', A_3', . . . These points lie on a horizontal line parallel to the horizontal sides of the rectangle. Through the points A_1', A_2', A_3', . . ., let us draw straight lines $P_1'Q_1'$, $P_2'Q_2'$, $P_3'Q_3'$, . . ., parallel to the other two sides of the rectangle, singling out the rectangle $P_1'Q_1'Q_2'P_2'$ which is obtained by making one turn of the sheet around the cylinder. When the sheet is wrapped around the cylinder, the segments $P_1'Q_1'$ and $P_2'Q_2'$ fall on the generator PQ of the cylinder, which passes through point A; the points A_1', A_2', A_3', . . ., merge and coincide with the point A of the cylinder.

The puncture marks made at point B will be the points B_1', B_2', B_3', . . ., of our sheet. Their arrangement is exactly analogous to

Fig. 19

Fig. 20

that of points A_1', A_2', A_3', . . . Let us draw lines connecting each of the points B_1', B_2', B_3', . . ., to A_1', and let us wrap the sheet onto the cylinder so that points A_1', A_2', A_3', . . ., fall onto point A, and points B_1', B_2', B_3', . . ., fall onto point B. The line segment $A_1'B_1'$ becomes the arc $\overset{\frown}{AB}$ of the helix with which we dealt before (Fig. 17).

For brevity let us say that the path $\overset{\frown}{AB}$ makes n *complete* positive (negative) revolutions around the axis of the cylinder if it makes exactly n positive (negative) revolutions, or else, more than n but less than $(n + 1)$ positive (negative) revolutions. When the plane is wrapped onto the cylinder, the segment $A_1'B_2'$ will also become an arc of a helix $(\overset{\frown}{AB})_1$ which joins the points A and B (Fig. 19); in exactly the same way, the segments $A_1'B_3'$, $A_1'B_4'$, . . ., become arcs of helices (Fig. 20) $(\overset{\frown}{AB})_2$, $(\overset{\frown}{AB})_3$, . . ., joining A and B. The arc $(AB)_1$ makes one complete positive revolution around the axis of the cylinder, the arcs $(\overset{\frown}{AB})_2$, $(\overset{\frown}{AB})_3$, . . ., make two, three, . . ., such complete revolutions, respectively.

The arc $(\widehat{AB})_1$ is the shortest arc joining the points A and B and making one complete positive revolution around the axis. Analogously, $(\widehat{AB})_2$, $(\widehat{AB})_3$, . . ., are the shortest arcs which make two, three, . . . , complete positive revolutions, respectively.

The arcs considered have been arcs of *right* helices. In exactly the same way, arcs of *left* helices which join the points A and B can be obtained which make one, two, three, . . ., complete negative revolutions around the axis of the cylinder (Fig. 21). Each of these arcs is a shortest path joining the points A and B and making the corresponding number of complete negative revolutions around the axis of the cylinder.

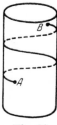

Fig. 21

Let us determine how a tightly stretched rubber string held at points A and B will arrange itself on the surface of the cylinder. As it is stretched, this string will arrange itself along one of the shortest paths, that is, along one of the helices which join the points A and B. If, for example, the string is wound on the cylinder so that, in moving along it, positive rotation is made around the axis (from right to left), then the string assumes the position of one of the helical arcs $\widehat{AB}$, $(\widehat{AB})_1$, $(\widehat{AB})_2$, . . . That is, it assumes the position $\widehat{AB}$ if the string makes less than one complete revolution around the axis of the cylinder; the position $(\widehat{AB})_1$ if it makes one complete revolution; the position $(\widehat{AB})_2$ if it makes two complete revolutions, and so on.

In fact, the string stretched between the points A_1' and one of the points B_1', B_2', B_3', . . ., on the plane rectangle will dispose itself along one of the segments $A_1'B_1'$, $A_1'B_2'$, $A_1'B_3'$, . . . If this sheet is now rolled onto the surface of the cylinder so that A_1' coincides with point A and the points B_1', B_2', B_3' with point B, then the stretched string assumes the position of the corresponding helical arc $\widehat{AB}$, $(\widehat{AB})_1$, $(\widehat{AB})_2$, . . .

14

3. Shortest Paths on Conic Surfaces

1. Shortest paths on a conic surface. Let two half-lines OA and ON originate from the point O. Let us rotate the half-line OA around the half-line ON, keeping the angle between the half-lines the same at all times. The surface generated by the half-line OA is called a *conic surface* (*the surface of a cone*) (Fig. 22). ON is called the *axis* of the cone. Half-lines originating from the point O and lying on the conic surface are called *generators* of the cone.†

If the plane which passes through two generators OA and OC also passes through the axis of the cone, then these generators are

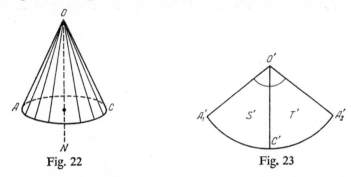

Fig. 22   Fig. 23

said to be *opposite*. The plane determined by two opposite generators divides the cone into two *congruent parts*. Let us cut the conic surface along a generator OA; after we have done this, the surface of the cone can be developed (unrolled) into a plane. The vertex O of the cone becomes a point O' of the plane; the generators of the cone become half-lines on the plane, originating at the point O'. The entire conic surface becomes the part of the plane included between the sides of some angle $A_1'O'A_2'$ in the plane (Fig. 23). This angle is called the *developed angle of the cone;* it is always less than 360°. The sides of the angle, $O'A_1'$ and $O'A_2'$, are formed from the generator OA along which the conic surface was cut. The generator OC opposite the generator OA becomes the bisector $O'C'$ of the angle $A_1'O'A_2'$. In fact, the two generators OA and OC divide the conic surface, cut along OA, into two congruent parts, S and T. When this surface is developed into the plane angle $A_1'O'A_2'$, the parts S and T of the cone become the halves S' and T'

† Figure 22 shows only a *part* of an infinite cone.

of this angle and the generator OC becomes the bisector $O'C'$ of this angle.

We have developed the cut conic surface into a plane. Let us now perform the reverse operation—roll the angle $A_1'O'A_2'$ into a cone. Now the point O' becomes the vertex of the cone O, and the sides $O'A_1'$ and $O'A_2'$ of the angle become one and the same generator.

Cut the whole plane along the side $O'A_1'$ of our angle. Roll the cut plane into a cone. The plane, generally speaking, will cover the cone several times. For example, if the developed angle of the cone equals 90°, then the plane will cover the conic surface four times; indeed, if at the point O' the half-lines $O'A_2'$, $O'A_3'$, $O'A_4'$ are drawn at angles 90°, 180°, 270° to $O'A_1'$, then with the rolling up of the cut

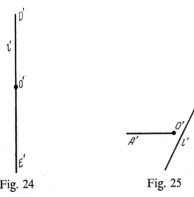

Fig. 24   Fig. 25

plane into a cone each of the angles $A_1'O'A_2'$, $A_2'O'A_3'$, $A_3'O'A_4'$, $A_4'O'A_1'$ covers the surface of the cone completely. In all we will have a fourfold covering of the cone by the cut plane. The half-lines $O'A_1'$, $O'A_2'$, $O'A_3'$, $O'A_4'$ of the plane become one and the same generator of the cone.

If the developed angle equals, for example, 100°, then the plane completely covers the conic surface three times and, in addition, part of the cone is covered a fourth time (the plane consists of three adjacent wedges, each with vertical angle 100° at O', each of which covers the whole of the conic surface once, and of an additional 60° wedge which also covers part of the surface).

2. Geodesic curves on a conic surface. Consider an arbitrary straight line l' on a plane. Let the straight line l' pass through the point O'; then it consists of two half-lines $O'D'$ and $O'E'$ (Fig. 24).

When the plane is rolled into a cone (when point O' coincides with the vertex O of the cone), each of the half-lines $O'D'$ and $O'E'$ becomes a generator of the cone. Our straight line is transformed into two generators.†

Now suppose the straight line l' does not pass through the point O' (Fig. 25). Let us cut the plane along the half-line $O'A'$ not intersecting l', and roll the cut plane into a conic surface. Depending on how large we make the vertical angle of the cone, our sheet of paper may roll round itself one or more times. In any case, the straight line l' becomes some curve l on the conic surface (Fig. 26). This curve l is called a *geodesic line* on the surface of the cone. Each line segment of the straight line l' becomes an arc of the curve l. Conversely, when the conic surface is developed into a plane, every

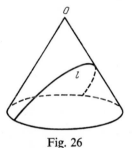

Fig. 26

arc of the curve l becomes a segment of the line l'. These curves on the surface of the cone play a role analogous to the helices on the surface of a cylinder.

Let us consider all possible paths joining points A and B of a conic surface and lying on the surface; let $\widehat{AB}$ denote the path having minimal length. Choose a generator OC of the cone which does not intersect $\widehat{AB}$, and develop the cone into a plane by cutting along OC. Then the path $\widehat{AB}$ becomes a plane curve $A'B'$; inasmuch as the path $\widehat{AB}$ is the shortest of the paths which lie on the conic surface and which join A and B, $A'B'$ is the shortest of the lines on the plane which join A' and B'. Thus, $A'B'$ is a straight line segment. The path $\widehat{AB}$, which is transformed into a straight line segment when

† The two generators may coincide. This happens if the developed conic angle, measured in degrees, is a divisor of $180°$, that is, if this angle equals $180°, 90°, 60°, \ldots$, in general, $180°/k$, where k is a whole number.

17

the conic surface is developed into a plane, is a geodesic arc. We shall see presently that the form of the geodesic depends essentially on the size of the developed conic angle.

3. Double points of geodesic curves. First let us introduce the following defintion. A point A is called a *double point of the curve q* if q passes through A twice.† In Fig. 27, the point B is a double point of the curve l; moving along the curve l in the direction indicated by the arrows, we pass through the point B twice.

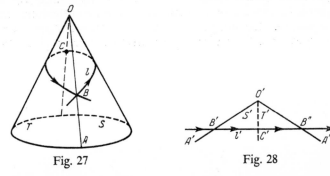

Fig. 27   Fig. 28

THEOREM 1. *If the developed conic angle is greater than or equal to 180°, then the geodesics on the cone do not have double points. If, however, the developed conic angle is less than 180°, then all the geodesics will have at least one double point.*

On a plane consider a point O' and a straight line l' which does not pass through O' (Fig. 28). If the plane is rolled into a cone so that O' coincides with the vertex O of the cone, then the straight line l' becomes a geodesic l.

Let C' be the foot of the perpendicular dropped from O' to l'. When the plane is rolled into a cone, the half-line $O'C'$ becomes a generator OC of the cone. The point C is sometimes called the *vertex* of the geodesic on the conic surface. Let us denote the opposite generator of the cone OA; OA and OC divide the surface of the cone into two congruent parts S and T. Cut the conic surface along the generator OA and develop it into a plane so that the vertex O of the cone again becomes the point O' and the generator OC becomes the half-line $O'C'$. Then the geodesic l again becomes the straight line l'. The whole of the conic surface becomes the

† Sometimes double points are called *nodes*.

18

portion of the plane included in the angle $A'O'A''$. The halves S and T of the conic surface become the halves S' and T' of this angle; the straight line $O'C'$ is the bisector of this angle.

Let us consider two cases.

(1) The angle $A'O'A''$ (the developed angle of the cone) is greater than or equal to 180° (Fig. 29). The straight line l' lies entirely inside this angle. If the angle is again rolled into a conic surface so that the sides $O'A'$ and $O'A''$ coincide with the generator OA, then the straight line l' once more becomes the geodesic l on the surface of the cone; different points of the straight line l' become different points of the cone; consequently, in this case l does not have any double points.

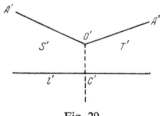

Fig. 29

(2) The angle $A'O'A''$ is less than 180°. The straight line l' is perpendicular to the bisector $O'C'$ of the angle, and cuts its sides at points which we shall designate by B' and B'' (Fig. 28).

Since the altitude $O'C'$ coincides with the bisector of the angle $B'O'B''$, the triangle $B'O'B''$ is isosceles. Let us roll the angle $A'O'A''$ onto the surface of a cone so that O' becomes the vertex of the cone, and both the sides $O'A'$, $O'A''$ of the angle become the generator OA. Because the segments $O'B'$ and $O'B''$ are equal, the points B' and B'' become a single point B on this generator (Fig. 27). The straight line l' becomes the geodesic l, the segment $B'C'$ of the straight line l', lying in the half S' of the angle $B'O'B''$, becomes the arc BC of the curve l, which joins the points B and C and which lies in the half S of the conic surface; analogously, the segment $B''C'$, lying in the half T' of the angle $B'O'B''$, becomes the arc BC of the line l, which joins the points B and C and which lies in the half T of the conic surface. The point B is a double point of the curve l. The segment $B'B''$ of the straight line l' becomes the arc BCB, which has the form of a loop with coinciding ends.

Let us determine how many double points a geodesic has. The

19

answer to this problem is given by the following theorem, which is more precise than the preceding theorem.

THEOREM 2. *Let the developed angle of a cone be* α (*degrees*).

(1) *If* 180 *is not divisible exactly by* α, *then the number of double points of the geodesic is equal to the integral part of the fraction* 180/α.

(2) *If* 180 *is divisible exactly by* α, *then the number of double points is* 180/α − 1.

If α > 180, then the integral part of the fraction 180/α equals zero; if α = 180, then 180/α − 1 = 0. Consequently, according to our theorem, in these cases the number of double points must be zero; this is merely a restatement of the first part of the preceding theorem.

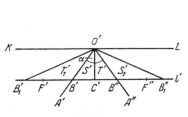

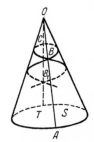

Fig. 30   Fig. 31

It remains to consider the case when α < 180. Let us use the notation of the previous theorem. The angle $A'O'A''$ (Fig. 30) is the developed angle of a cone. Through the point O' let us draw the perpendicular $O'C'$ to the straight line l' and the line KL parallel to the line l'. KL divides the plane into two half-planes. Let us consider only that half-plane in which the line l' lies. From the point O' in this half-plane we draw half-lines which make angles with the half-line $O'C'$ that are multiples of $\frac{1}{2}α$. These will be the half-lines $O'B'$, $O'B''$, $O'B_1'$, $O'B_1''$, . . ., which intersect the straight line l' at points B', B'', B_1', B_1'', . . . We note that $O'B' = O'B''$, $O'B_1' = O'B_1''$, . . . We now roll up our half-plane into a cone so that the point O' coincides with the vertex of the cone O, and the half-line $O'C'$ falls along the generator OC (Fig. 31). The regions within the angles of our half-plane equal to $\frac{1}{2}α$ and included between neighboring half-lines $O'B_1'$, $O'B'$, $O'C'$, $O'B''$, $O'B_1''$, . . ., now cover both halves of the conic surface S and T several times. In

20

other words, the region within the angle S' will fall on the half S of the cone; the regions within the angles T_1' and T' adjacent to it on the half T of the cone, and so on. Since the half-line $O'C'$ lies along the generator OC, the half-lines $O'B'$, $O'B''$ lie along the opposite generator OA, the half-lines $O'B_1'$, $O'B_1''$ again lie along OC, and so on.

Because $O'B' = O'B''$ and $O'B_1' = O'B_1''$, the points B' and B'', B_1' and B_1'', . . ., falling on the same generator, coincide in pairs; point B' coincides with B'' and also with point B of the generator OA; B_1' and B_1'' coincide at the point B_1 of the generator OC, and so on. Consequently, points B, B_1, . . ., are double points of the geodesic curve l into which the line l_1 is transformed when the half-plane is rolled into a cone. The number of these points is equal to the number of half-lines $O'B'$, $O'B_1'$, . . ., inside the right angle $KO'C'$. Since these half-lines form angles with $O'C'$ which are multiples of $\frac{1}{2}\alpha$ and which are less than 90°, the total number of them is the largest whole number by which α can be multiplied so that the product is still less than 180. In other words, if 180 is not exactly divisible by α, then the number of these half-lines equals the integral part of the fraction $180/\alpha$. If, however, 180 is divisible by α, then their number equals $(180/\alpha) - 1$.

To complete the proof of the theorem it remains to be shown that the double points of the geodesic curve are precisely those points which are obtained by the merging of the points B_i' and B_i'' of the straight line l'. Now a double point of the geodesic l is obtained if two points of our line l' become one and the same point of the cone when the half-plane is rolled into a cone. For this to happen, both the points must be equidistant from O' and lie on the line l'. Thus, these two points must be situated on l' symmetrically with respect to C'. Let one of them, which we shall call F' (see Fig. 30), lie to the left of C', and the other F'' to the right. If the point F' does not coincide with any one of the points B', B'', B_1', B_1'', . . ., then, if we denote the angles $C'O'B'$, $B'O'B_1'$, . . ., $C'O'B''$, $B''O'B_1''$, . . ., by the corresponding letters S_i' and T_i' (Fig. 30), the point F' must lie inside one of the angles S_i'. If the point F' lies inside the angle S_i', then its symmetrical point F'' lies inside the angle T_i'; that is, when the half-plane is rolled into a cone, the point F' becomes a point situated inside the half-cone S, while the point F'' becomes a point that lies inside the half-cone T. Conversely, if the point F' becomes a point that lies inside the half-cone T, then the point F'' becomes a point that lies inside the half-cone S. In both

21

these cases, F' and F'' are transformed into different points of the cone. Thus, except for the double points obtained by the merging of the pairs B' and B'', B_1' and B_1'', ..., there are no new double points on the geodesic l. The theorem is proved.

Let us now consider the strip that lies between the parallel straight lines KL and l'. We suggest that the reader investigate how this strip will fall upon the conic surface for different values of the developed angle α of the cone (when $\alpha > 180°$, $\alpha = 180°$, $180° > \alpha > 90°$, $\alpha = 90°$, $90° > \alpha > 60°$, and so on).

Repeating the arguments at the end of Section 2, we see that on the surface of a cone a stretched elastic string will lie along a geodesic line.

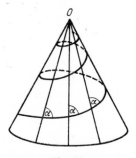
Fig. 32

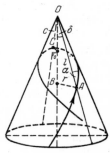
Fig. 33

Note. Helices may be defined on cones, just as they are on cylinders, to be curves intersecting all the generators in equal angles α can also be considered (Fig. 32). When $\alpha = 0$ and $\alpha = 90°$, the helices on the cone become generators and circular sections, respectively. When $\alpha \neq 0$, the helices on the cone are not geodesics; in this they differ from helices on the surface of a cylinder.

4. Clairaut's theorem for the case of geodesics on a cone. Let C be the vertex of a geodesic s on the surface of a cone, let c denote the length of the segment OC, and let r_0 be the distance from C to the axis of the cone (Fig. 33). The geodesic is perpendicular to the generator OC at the point C. Further, let A be an *arbitrary* point on the geodesic, r the distance from A to the axis of the cone, α the angle between the geodesic s and the generator OA at the point A, and l the length of the segment OA. Then the following relationship holds:

$$l \sin \alpha = c. \tag{1}$$

22

To prove formula (1) let us unroll the surface of the cone into a plane (Fig. 34). Then OC and OA become $O'C'$ and $O'A'$ (the lengths of c and l are preserved), the arc $\widehat{AC}$ of the geodesic s becomes the segment $A'C'$ of a straight line, and $O'C'$ will be per-

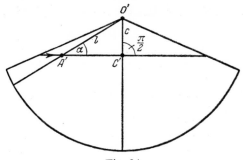

Fig. 34

pendicular to the straight line $A'C'$; the angle at the vertex A' of the triangle $A'O'C'$ equals α. From the triangle $A'O'C'$, we obtain

$$l \sin \alpha = c.$$

Let us notice that if δ is the angle between the generator of the cone and its axis (see Fig. 33), then $r = l \sin \delta$. Multiplying both sides of equation (1) by $\sin \delta$, we obtain

$$l \sin \delta \cdot \sin \alpha = c \sin \delta$$

or
$$r \sin \alpha = c_1, \tag{2}$$

where $c_1 = c \sin \delta$—a constant value for the geodesic.

The last equality proves the following proposition.

THEOREM 3. *For all points A of a geodesic s on a conic surface, the value of the expression r* $\sin \alpha$*, where r is the distance of the point A from the axis of the cone and* α *is the angle between the generator OA and the geodesic s, is a constant:*

$$r \sin \alpha = \text{const.} \tag{3}$$

This theorem is a special case of Clairaut's theorem (see Section 10).

A cylinder can be considered as the limiting case of a cone (when the vertex of the cone moves to infinity). A helix on a cylinder corresponds to a geodesic on a cone. Formula (3) obviously remains valid for a cylinder as well: the distance r of all points on the cylinder from the axis is constant, and the angle α between the helix and the generators of the cylinder is also constant for all points on the helix.

4. Shortest Paths on Spherical Surfaces

1. The length of a curve. In our investigation of shortest paths on the surfaces of cylinders and cones we made use of the fact that cylindrical and conical surfaces can be unrolled into part of a plane. But this method cannot be applied in the investigation of shortest paths on the surface of a sphere, since a sphere cannot be developed into part of a plane.

We now recall the following fact from elementary geometry: The shortest path joining distinct points A and B, is the segment AB of the straight line through them. This follows from the postulate which asserts that one side of a triangle is less than the sum of the other two. On the basis of this last postulate we prove that the segment of the straight line AB is shorter than any broken line $A_0A_1A_2 \ldots A_{n-1}A_n$, which has the same ends $A_0 = A$ and $A_n = B$ (Fig. 35). In fact, we only shorten, never lengthen, the broken line

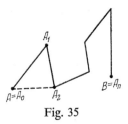

Fig. 35

if two of its adjacent segments, say A_0A_1 and A_1A_2, are replaced by the segment A_0A_2 (because the side A_0A_2 of the triangle $A_0A_1A_2$ is less than the sum of the sides A_0A_1 and A_1A_2).† Thus we replace the broken line $A_0A_1A_2 \ldots A_{n-1}A_n$ by the broken line $A_0A_2 \ldots A_{n-1}A_n$ which has one side less. Analogously, in this last broken line the two adjacent segments A_0A_2 and A_2A_3 can be replaced by

† If the points A_0, A_1, A_2 lie in a straight line, then the sum of the lengths of the two segments A_0A_1 and A_1A_2 equals the length of the segment A_0A_2. Thus, in replacing the two segments A_0A_1 and A_1A_2 by the single segment A_0A_2 we do not increase the length of the broken line. This note applies also to the discussion that follows.

one side A_0A_3 without increasing the length of the broken line. We then obtain the broken line $A_0A_3 \ldots A_{n-1}A_n$, in which the number of segments has been reduced once again by one. In this way we can successively reduce the number of the segments of the broken line until we obtain a single segment—the segment $A_0A_n = AB$. Thus, with each change from one broken line to the next, the length can only decrease (sometimes this length will remain unchanged; but it cannot remain unchanged for every replacement because this is possible only when all the points $A_0, A_1, \ldots, A_n$ lie in the same straight line, which has been excluded). It follows that the original broken line was longer than the segment AB. In elementary geometry it is proved only that the segment AB of the straight line is shorter than any broken line that joins the same points A and B.

To obtain the analogous assertion for an arbitrary curve joining the points A and B, it is first necessary to define precisely what we mean by the length of a curve. In elementary geometry the length (circumference) of a circle is defined to be the limit of the perimeters of the inscribed polygons, as the number of sides of the polygon tends to infinity and the length of the greatest side tends to zero.

The length of an arbitrary curve can be defined analogously. Suppose that we are given a curve q joining the points A and B (Fig. 36). Let us move along this curve in the direction from A to

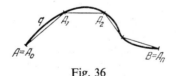

Fig. 36

B and mark off successively $(n + 1)$ points $A_0 = A, A_1, A_2, A_3, \ldots, A_n = B$. Let us join these points successively by straight line segments; we obtain the broken line $A_0A_1A_2 \ldots A_n$, which we shall call a *broken line inscribed in the given curve*. Now construct a broken line inscribed in the curve q and let the number of segments making up the broken line increase without limit. Moreover, construct these broken lines so that as the number of segments increases without limit the *length of the longest side tends to zero*. It can be shown that under certain conditions the lengths of the inscribed broken lines tend to a limit; *it is this limiting number which is taken as the length of the curve.*

Since the line segment AB is shorter than any broken line joining the points A and B, and since the length of a curve joining these points is the limit of the lengths of broken lines inscribed in the curve, it follows that the line segment joining A and B is the shortest of all paths that join A and B.

2. Shortest paths on the surface of a sphere. Let us turn now to the problem of finding shortest paths on the surface of a sphere. Note that if A and B are two different points on the surface of a sphere, then one and only one great circle can be drawn through A and B —provided, of course, that A and B are not diametrically opposite; if these two points do lie at opposite ends of a diameter, then there are an infinite number of great circles passing through them. For the time being we shall exclude the latter case entirely; when we speak of two points on the surface of a sphere we shall tacitly assume that the line segment joining these two points is not a diameter of the sphere.

Given two points A and B on the surface of a sphere, let us draw the great circle passing through them. Since A and B do not lie at opposite ends of a diameter, they divide this great circle into two unequal arcs; let us denote the smaller of these two arcs by $\overset{\frown}{AB}$.

Suppose we are given three points A, B, and C on the surface of a sphere, and suppose that these points have been joined to one another by the arcs of great circles $\overset{\frown}{AB}$, $\overset{\frown}{BC}$, $\overset{\frown}{CA}$. These three arcs form a figure ABC called a *spherical triangle*; the arcs $\overset{\frown}{AB}$, $\overset{\frown}{BC}$, $\overset{\frown}{CA}$ are the *sides* of the spherical triangle.

There is a theorem for spherical triangles which is the analogue of the result in plane geometry asserting that the sum of any two sides of a triangle is greater than the third side.

THEOREM. *The sum of any two sides of a spherical triangle is greater than the third side.*

Consider a spherical triangle ABC on the surface of a sphere with center O (Fig. 37). The side $\overset{\frown}{AB}$ of the spherical triangle is an arc of a great circle, that is, of a circle lying on the sphere and having center O; in the plane of this circle, the arc AB corresponds to the central angle AOB. Similarly, the central angles BOC and COA correspond to the sides $\overset{\frown}{BC}$ and $\overset{\frown}{CA}$ in their respective planes. The lengths of the sides $\overset{\frown}{AB}$, $\overset{\frown}{BC}$, $\overset{\frown}{CA}$, since they are arcs of great circles having equal radii, are proportional to the central angles AOB, BOC, COA.

The three planes of these great circles form a trihedral angle with vertex at the point O and with face angles AOB, BOC, COA. The lengths of the sides of the triangle ABC are proportional to the corresponding face angles of this trihedral angle. Since any face angle of a trihedral angle is less than the sum of the other two face angles, an analogous inequality holds for the sides of the spherical triangle. This completes the proof of our theorem.

Suppose we are given a sequence of points A_0, A_1, A_2, A_3, . . ., A_n on a sphere which are joined by arcs of great circles $\overparen{A_0A_1}$, $\overparen{A_1A_2}$, $\overparen{A_2A_3}$, . . ., $\overparen{A_{n-1}A_n}$. These arcs form a *spherical broken line* joining the points A_0 and A_n (Fig. 38).

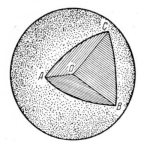
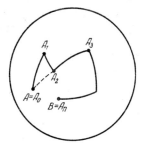

Fig. 37   Fig. 38

For a plane, the fact that one side of a triangle is less than the sum of the other two sides leads to the theorem that the straight line segment AB is shorter than any broken line which joins the same points A and B. Analogously, for a spherical surface, from the fact that one side of a spherical triangle is less than the sum of the other two sides, it follows that the arc $\overparen{AB}$ of a great circle joining points A and B is less than any spherical broken line which joins the same points. Moreover, for a spherical surface, as for the plane, the lengths of curves that join two points A and B are obtained as the limits of the lengths of spherical broken lines that join these points. Since the arc $\overparen{AB}$ of a great circle is shorter than all the spherical broken lines that join A and B, it is also shorter than any of the curves that join these points.

The proof that the arc $\overparen{AB}$ is shorter than any spherical broken line which joins the points A and B is essentially a repetition of the proof of the analogous theorem for broken lines on a plane. Let the arc $\overarc{AB}$ and the spherical broken line $A_0A_1A_2A_3 \ldots A_n$, where $A_0 = A$ and $A_n = B$, be given.

In the spherical triangle $A_0A_1A_2$, the side $\overarc{A_0A_2}$ may be shorter, and is certainly not longer, than the sum of the sides $\overarc{A_0A_1}$ and $\overarc{A_1A_2}$.† Let us substitute the arc $\overarc{A_0A_2}$ for the two segments $\overarc{A_0A_1}$ and $\overarc{A_1A_2}$. We obtain a new broken line $A_0A_2A_3 \ldots A_n$, which may be shorter than the original one, and which contains one less segment. Next let us substitute the single side $\overarc{A_0A_3}$ for the two sides $\overarc{A_0A_2}$ and $\overarc{A_2A_3}$. By this operation the length of the broken line can only decrease or remain unchanged. Let us continue with analogous operations (substituting one arc for two adjacent arcs of the broken line). With each reduction in the number of sides, the length of the broken line can only decrease or remain unchanged. We shall obtain new broken lines, joining A and B, each with a smaller number of sides, until finally we arrive at a broken line of only one segment, that is, the arc $\overarc{AB}$ itself. In the course of this process the length of the broken line each time decreases or remains unchanged. But the length of the broken line cannot remain unchanged after every step since this would mean that the points A_0, A_1, $\ldots$, A_n all lie on the arc $\overarc{AB}$ of the same great circle, which has been excluded. Therefore *the length of the original broken line $A_0A_1 \ldots A_n$ is greater than the length of the arc $\overarc{AB}$.*

Let us now examine the case when the points A and B lie at the ends of the same diameter of the sphere. In this case there exist an infinite number of arcs of great circles which join A and B and which have AB as the diameter. All of these arcs have the same length. On the other hand, any other curve q, which joins the same points A and B, has a greater length than a semicircle of a great circle. In fact, let the point C (different from A and B) lie on q and divide this curve into two curves (AC) and (CB). Let us draw the

† If the points A_0, A_1, and A_2 lie on the same great circle, then the side $\overarc{A_0A_2}$ either equals the sum of the sides $\overarc{A_0A_1}$ and $\overarc{A_1A_2}$, if this sum is less than a semicircle, or is less than it, if this sum is greater than a semicircle. So whenever the two sides $\overarc{A_0A_1}$ and $\overarc{A_1A_2}$ are replaced by the single segment $\overarc{A_0A_2}$ the length of the broken line can only decrease or remain unchanged. This note applies also to the discussion that follows.

28

semicircle of the great circle $\overset{\frown}{ACB}$; it consists of the two arcs $\overset{\frown}{AC}$ and $\overset{\frown}{CB}$. Each of these arcs is shorter than any other curve on the surface of the sphere which joins the same points. Because our curve q is not a semicircle, at least one of its parts (AC) or (CB) fails to coincide with the corresponding arc $\overset{\frown}{AC}$ or $\overset{\frown}{CB}$. For example, suppose (AC) does not coincide with $\overset{\frown}{AC}$. Then the length of (AC) is greater than the length of $\overset{\frown}{AC}$. Further, the length of (CB) is either greater than the length of $\overset{\frown}{CB}$ (if they do not coincide) or equal to it (if (CB) coincides with $\overset{\frown}{CB}$). It follows that the total length of q is greater than the length of $\overset{\frown}{ACB}$.

For two diametrically opposite points A and B, there exist an infinite number of shortest curves which connect these points; these curves are all the semicircles of great circles joining the points A and B.

3. Additional notes. The surface of a sphere cannot be developed into a part of a plane without deforming it, that is, without changing the lengths of curves lying on it. However, a very narrow strip situated on the surface of a sphere along some curve q can be developed onto a plane and suffer only very small distortions in the lengths of curves lying in the strip. The narrower the strip taken on the sphere, the smaller the distortions and the greater the accuracy of the development of this strip on the plane. Expressed in the jargon of the theory of limits, the distortion of the lengths of curves on the strip has a higher order of smallness than the width of the strip.

If a narrow strip lying on the surface of a sphere is developed onto a plane, then the arc of a great circle included in this strip becomes a straight line segment (or vice versa).†

In fact, the arc $\overset{\frown}{AB}$ of a great circle on a spherical strip is shorter than all other curves lying on the strip and joining points A and B. If, when the strip is developed onto a plane, the points A and B are transformed into A' and B', then the arc $\overset{\frown}{AB}$ is transformed into a curve which connects A' and B' on the plane and, in addition, shorter than the neighboring plane curves which join these same points; consequently $\overset{\frown}{AB}$ is transformed into the straight line segment $A'B'$.

COROLLARY. On the surface of the sphere cut a narrow strip around a great circle and develop it onto a plane. This strip becomes a plane straight strip; the great circle becomes the center line of the strip. Conversely, if a narrow straight strip (ribbon) is wrapped around the surface of a sphere, it will contact this surface along a great circle (Fig. 39).

† This statement is true to as high a degree of approximation as we wish, depending upon the width of the strip.

Let us see now what happens if we transform a narrow strip containing an arc of a small circle q (that is, a circle on the surface of the sphere which is not a great circle).

Let us note first of all the following circumstance. Cut a conic surface by a plane perpendicular to the axis of the cone. This plane intersects

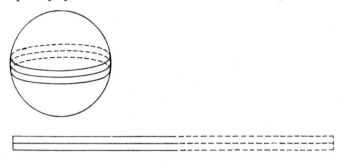

Fig. 39

the conic surface along a circle q. The segments of generators from th vertex O of the cone to the circle q are equal (for example, in Fig. 40, $OA = OB = OC$). If the conic surface is cut along the generator OC and this surface is developed onto a plane, the circle q will become an arc of the circle q' with radius equal to OC. The narrow strip on the surface of the cone having the circle q as its center line develops on the plane into a strip having an arc q' as its center line (Fig. 41).

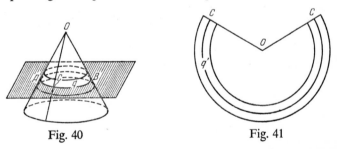

Fig. 40   Fig. 41

Let us return now to a spherical surface (Fig. 42). Draw the diameter AB through the center O_1 of the small circle p_1 and the center O of the sphere; draw the great circle p with diameter AB to intersect the small circle p_1 at a point C. Let r be the radius of p_1, R the radius of the sphere, α the angle O_1CO. We have

$$\cos \alpha = \frac{r}{R}.$$

30

Draw the tangent CD to p at the point C until it intersects at point D with the extension of the diameter AB. We have $\angle CDO = \angle O_1CO = \alpha$ (because the corresponding sides of these angles are perpendicular). From the triangle OCD we have

$$CD = R \cot \alpha = R \frac{\cos \alpha}{\sqrt{(1 - \cos^2 \alpha)}}$$

$$= R \left\{ \frac{r}{R} \middle/ \sqrt{\left[1 - \left(\frac{r}{R} \right)^2 \right]} \right\} = \frac{rR}{\sqrt{(R^2 - r^2)}}.$$

Rotate the drawing around the axis AB. The straight line CD now generates a conic surface; the circle p describes a sphere of radius R. These conic and spherical surfaces touch along the circle p_1.

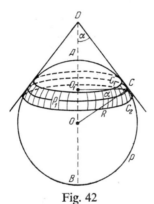

Fig. 42

The small arc C_1C_2 of the circle p, which contains the point C, can be considered as coinciding with a small segment of the tangent.† Rotating this arc around AB we obtain a spherical strip that contains the small circle p_1. This strip can be considered as coinciding with a strip on the cone,‡ which touches our sphere along the circle p_1 (this strip on the surface of the cone is formed by the rotation of the segment of the tangent with which we considered the arc C_1C_2 to coincide). If this strip is cut along C_1C_2 and developed onto a plane, then the circle p_1 becomes the arc of a circle with radius equal to CD, that is, of radius

$$l = \frac{Rr}{\sqrt{(R^2 - r^2)}},$$

† These coincide if values of a higher order of smallness than the length C_1C_2 are disregarded.
‡ Coinciding in the same sense.

31

while the narrow strip on the spherical surface which has the circle p_1 as its center line develops into a plane strip, enclosing the arc of a circle of radius l. The case where the plane strip is a straight line (Fig. 39 instead of Fig. 41) is the limiting case of this situation when r tends to R: our equation shows that in this case we should regard the strip as the limiting case of a circular strip as its radius l tends to infinity. ...

Conversely, let us roll onto the surface of a sphere of radius R a narrow plane strip which has an arc of a circle of radius l as its center line. It will touch the spherical surface along a small circle. The radius of this circle can be determined from the equation

$$l = \frac{Rr}{\sqrt{(R^2 - r^2)}}.$$

It is not difficult to find that

$$r = \frac{Rl}{\sqrt{(R^2 + l^2)}}.$$

2

SOME PROPERTIES OF PLANE AND SPACE CURVES AND RELATED PROBLEMS

5. Tangents and Normals to Plane Curves and Related Problems

1. Tangents to a curve. Consider a curve q in a plane or in space, and let A be a point on it (Fig. 43). Select another point B on the same curve q. Let us draw the straight line n determined by the points A and B. A line such as n (intersecting q in two distinct points) is called a *secant*. If we allow B to move along the curve q

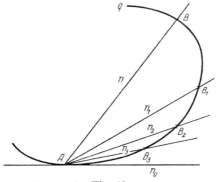

Fig. 43

toward the point A, the secant n will rotate about point A. As B gets closer and closer to A, the secant approaches a limiting position —some straight line n_0. The line n_0 is called the *tangent* to the curve q at the point A. If we imagine that B is a point mass, then as B moves along q, should B break away from the curve at A, it would fly off along the tangent line to q at A.

2. Normals to a curve. Let q be a curve lying in a plane (such a curve we shall call a plane curve). We shall call the straight line MN which passes through the point A and is perpendicular to the tangent n_0 to the curve q at the point A the *normal* to the curve q at the point A (Fig. 44).

3. The shortest distance between two curves. Consider a curve q and a moving point A whose path of motion is restricted to q. Let P be a force acting on the point A (Fig. 45). We resolve the force P into two components: a *tangential* component P_1 (directed along the tangent to the curve q at point A), and a *normal* component P_2 (directed along the normal at A). The tangential component moves A along the curve q. Hence, *the point A is in equilibrium just in case*

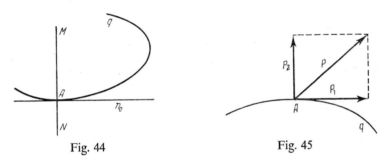

Fig. 44   Fig. 45

the magnitude of the tangential component P_1 is zero, that is, when P is identical with the component P_2, acting along the normal to q at A.

Let q and q_1 be two curves. Consider all line segments AB with one end point A on q and the other end point B on q_1; let us determine the shortest such segment. Imagine that an elastic string has small metal rings at both its ends, one ring being threaded along q and the other on q_1. The tension in the string forces it to move until it has assumed the position in which the tension is least. Since the tension in the string increases as the length increases, the position of least tension is the position in which the length of the string is least. Let A_0 and B_0 be the positions of the rings on curves q and q_1 once the string is in equilibrium. Since the string is in equilibrium, so is its end point A_0. The tension in the string is direct along the line segment A_0B_0; hence the segment A_0B_0 must be the normal to q at A_0. In the same way, we see that A_0B_0 is the normal to q_1 at B_0. Thus *the shortest line segment joining points of two curves is a*

34

common normal to these curves. Analogously, *the shortest of the line segments joining the points of a curve q to a point A is the normal drawn from A to q.*

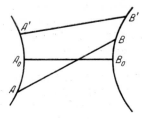

Fig. 46

4. The problem of reflection. Let q be a fixed curve. Let us consider all those curves ACB which join two given points A and B and which have a point C in common with the curve q, or, so to speak, those curves which connect points A and B and reflect from the curve q.

Let us consider an elastic string ACB held at its ends A and B and having a point C which moves along the curve q (Fig. 47). Let AC_0B be the shortest of the lines joining the points A and B by reflection from the curve q (C_0 is a point on the curve q). The string is in equilibrium in the position AC_0B. Obviously, both parts AC_0 and

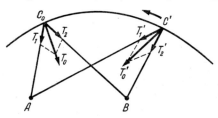

Fig. 47

C_0B of the shortest curve are straight line segments. The point C_0 of the string on the curve is in equilibrium; therefore, at this point the force from the tension of the string is of equal magnitude in both directions along the string.† The force T_1 directed along the segment C_0A is equal to the force T_2 along the segment C_0B, and their resultant T_0 is directed along the bisector of the angle AC_0B. By the equilibrium condition, T_0 is directed along the normal to the curve q at point C_0. Hence the bisector of the angle AC_0B is the

† The tension is the same for all points of the string.

normal to the curve q at point C_0. If the point C is elsewhere, say at C', the resultant T_0' of the tensions at C' has a component tangential to the curve, so that C' will slide along it (Fig. 47).

The shortest of all curved lines which join the points A and B by reflection from the curve q is the broken line AC_0B with its vertex at a point C_0 on the curve q at which the normal to this curve coincides with the bisector of the angle AC_0B.

5. Shortest paths in a region. Let us consider regions in a plane which are bounded by some curves. The regions can be finite (region I in Fig. 48), or infinite (for example, region II in the same figure, which is obtained by excluding region I from the plane).

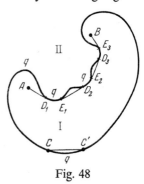

Fig. 48

Let us seek the shortest of the paths in region I which join two points A and B in this region. This path $\overset{\frown}{AB}$ is the equilibrium position of a flexible string situated in region I with end points fixed at points A and B. (We suppose there to be a wall constructed along the boundary so that the string cannot slip outside region I at any point.) The string can contain parts of the boundary q of region I.

Let $s_0 = AD_1E_1D_2E_2 \ldots D_nE_nB$ be the shortest of the curves s. It consists of parts $\overset{\frown}{D_1E_1}$, $\overset{\frown}{D_2E_2}$, . . ., $\overset{\frown}{D_nE_n}$ of the boundary (in Fig. 48, $n = 3$) and curves $\overset{\frown}{AD_1}$, $\overset{\frown}{E_1D_2}$, . . ., $\overset{\frown}{E_nB}$, which (except for their end points) lie completely inside I. Obviously, each of the lines AD_1, E_1D_2, . . ., E_nB is a straight line segment.

Each part of the boundary D_1E_1, D_2E_2, . . ., D_nE_n, which forms part of s_0, is concave with respect to I. In fact, for each very small part CC' of the boundary q which is convex with respect to I, a

36

chord CC' lies inside I; this chord is shorter than the arc $\overset{\frown}{CC'}$; therefore, if the line s_0 contains such an arc $\overset{\frown}{CC'}$ of the boundary, then we can shorten s_0 by replacing the arc $\overset{\frown}{CC'}$ by the chord CC', which lies in I. Thus the shortest line can contain only those parts of the boundary that are concave with respect to I.

The segments AD_1, E_1D_2, . . ., $E_{n-1}D_n$, E_nB, which form part of s_0, touch the curve q at the points D_1, E_1, D_2, E_2, . . ., D_n, E_n, respectively (Fig. 48). In fact, at the point D_1, for example, two parts of the string are connected: the segment AD_1 and the part $\overset{\frown}{D_1E_1}$ of the curve q. The tension T_1 of part AD_1 is directed along the segment D_1A (Fig. 49), and the tension T_2 of part $\overset{\frown}{D_1E_1}$ is directed

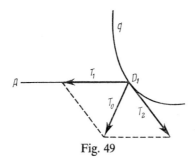

Fig. 49

along the tangent to q at point D_1. If the angle between the directions of T_1 and T_2 differs from $180°$, then the resultant T_0 of the forces T_1 and T_2 will displace the point D_1 (Fig. 49), that is, the string will not be in a position of equilibrium. Hence this angle equals $180°$, that is, the segment AD_1 is tangent to the curve q at point D_1. Thus the shortest line in region I which joins the points A and B consists of the tangential segments AD_1, E_1D_2, . . ., E_nB and bits of the boundary D_1E_1, D_2E_2, . . ., D_nE_n which are concave with respect to I.

6. Some Observations from the Theory of Plane and Space Curves

1. The osculating circle. Let a plane curve q (Fig. 50) be given. At the point A of this curve let us draw the tangent KL and the normal MN. Let us consider those circles which are tangent to the straight line *KL* at the point *A* (that is, have a common tangent with the curve *q* at point *A*); obviously, their centers lie on the normal *MN*.

Among all these circles there is one that has the "closest contact" with the curve *q* at the point *A*. (In our drawing this is the circle *r*.) This circle is called the *osculating circle*. A small arc $\overset{\frown}{BC}$ of the curve *q* including the point *A* can be thought of as approximating an arc of the osculating circle *r*. The smaller the arc $\overset{\frown}{BC}$ the more closely it approximates an arc of the circle *r*. The center of the osculating circle *r* is sometimes called the *center of curvature* of *q* at the point *A*. Thus a small arc $\overset{\frown}{BC}$ of the curve *q* which contains the point *A* can be approximately considered to be an arc of a circle which has its center at the center of curvature.

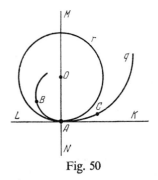

Fig. 50

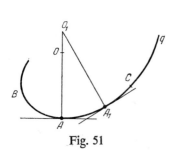

Fig. 51

The center of a circle lies at the intersection of two of its radii, and, because the radii are normal to the circle, we can say that the center of a circle lies at the intersection of its normals.

Let us now consider an arbitrary curve *q*, and on it a point *A* and a small arc $\overset{\frown}{BC}$ which includes this point (Fig. 51). This arc can be thought of as approximating an arc of the osculating circle with center at the point *O*. How is the center of this circle (the center of curvature) to be found?

Since we can consider the arc $\overset{\frown}{BC}$ to be approximately an arc of the osculating circle, we can use the following method of construction for the center of curvature. Let us draw the normals to the curve *q* at the point *A* and at some nearby point A_1 of the curve. These normals intersect at a point O_1. If we consider our arc $\overset{\frown}{BC}$ to be an arc of the osculating circle, then, by the previous reasoning,

38

the point O_1 will be the center of the osculating circle (the center of curvature).

Note. Our construction for the center of the osculating circle will be approximate. The smaller the arc $\overset{\frown}{BC}$, the more accurate our construction. We can (exactly) define the center of curvature of the curve q at the point A as the limiting position which the point of intersection of the normal at the point A and the normal at a neighboring point A_1 approaches as the point A_1 approaches the point A. The closer the point A_1, at which we draw the second normal, is to point A, the closer the point of intersection of these normals—the point O_1—is to the limiting position, the point O. The osculating circle can be defined as the circle of radius OA and center O.

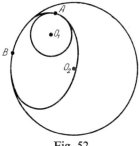

Fig. 52

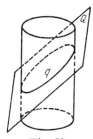

Fig. 53

EXAMPLE. In Fig. 52 the centers of curvature and the osculating circles at the vertices B and A of an ellipse are constructed using the approximate method described above.

2. Space curves. So far we have considered only curves in a plane. Let us turn now to the study of space curves. It is obvious that there are curves that cannot be placed in a plane. Such, for example, are helices.

In fact, suppose q is a helix on a given cylindrical surface. If q were a plane curve, then q would be the intersection of the plane Q in which it lies and the given cylindrical surface. There are two cases to consider: either the plane Q intersects the axis of the cylinder in a single point, or else Q is parallel to the axis. In the first case, Q intersects the surface of the cylinder in a closed curve (a circle or an ellipse; see Fig. 53); but then q could not be a helix, since a helix is not a closed curve. Now consider the case in which Q is parallel to the axis of the cylinder (we include here the case in which the axis lies in the plane Q). Let d be the distance from the axis of the cylinder to the plane Q, and r the radius of a right section of the cylinder. If d is less than r, then Q intersects the surface of the cylinder in two parallel lines (generators); if d is equal to r, then the intersection is a single straight line; finally, if d is greater than r, Q has no points in common with the cylinder. In any case, the intersection of Q and the surface of the cylinder will not be a helix.

The definition of a *tangent* to a space curve is analogous to that for a tangent to a plane curve. We define a *normal* to a space curve q at a point A on q to be any line passing through A and perpendicular to the tangent at the point A. Clearly, there will be an infinite number of lines which are normal to q at A. These lines form a plane that is perpendicular to the tangent line at the point A (Fig. 54).

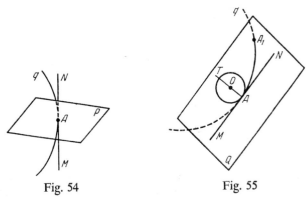

Fig. 54   Fig. 55

3. The osculating plane. Let A be a point on a curve q and MN the straight line tangent to q at A (Fig. 55). On the curve q take a point A_1 very close to the point A. The small arc $\overparen{AA_1}$ of the space curve q can be considered as approximating an arc of a plane curve. The plane Q determined by the tangent line MN and the point A_1 can be thought of as approximating the plane in which the small arc $\overparen{AA_1}$ of our curve lies. Plane Q is called the *osculating plane to the curve q at the point A*.

Note. Let us give an exact definition of the osculating plane. Let us draw the plane Q' determined by the tangent line MN and the point A_1 on q. Let the point A_1 approach A by moving along the curve q. As A_1 approaches A, the plane Q' rotates about the line MN and approaches a certain limiting plane Q. This limiting plane is the *osculating plane* to q at the point A. With this definition we see that if the point A_1 is very close to A, then the plane Q' determined by MN and point A_1 is in almost the same position as the osculating plane Q. In other words, we can think of the plane Q' as approximating the osculating plane.

4. The principal normal. The line AT which is normal to a curve q at a point A and which lies in the osculating plane at point A is called the *principal normal* to q at point A (Fig. 55). If the curve q is a plane curve, then the plane in which q lies is the osculating plane for q at each point of q, and the principal normals to q are those normals which lie in the plane of q.

5. The osculating circle for a space curve. A small arc of a space curve, containing a point A of the curve, can be considered to approximate an arc lying in the osculating plane Q to the curve q at point A. Such an arc in the plane Q can be thought of as approximating an arc of a circle lying in Q and having its tangent at A coinciding with the tangent to q at A. The circle of which this small arc is a part is called the *osculating circle* of the space curve q at the point A. As before, this is only an "approximate definition". As we take our arcs smaller and smaller, they approximate more and more closely to arcs of the osculating circles. These observations from the theory of space curves will prove useful in our later work.

7. Some Observations from the Theory of Surfaces

1. Tangent planes and normal planes to a surface. Let us consider a surface S and a point A on it (Fig. 56). A small patch of the surface around the point A can be thought of as approximating a portion of a plane Q—called the *tangent plane* to S at the point A. More exactly: if, for each curve q lying on the surface S and passing through A, the line tangent to q at A lies in a given plane Q, then Q is the *tangent plane* to the surface S at the point A.

If on the surface S we have two curves q and q_1 which pass through point A and which have non-coinciding tangents LL_1 and MM_1 at point A, then the tangent plane Q is the plane which is determined by the straight lines LL_1 and MM_1. The straight line passing through A and perpendicular to the tangent plane Q at point A of the surface S is called the *normal* to the surface S at point A.

The normal AN to a surface is a normal to all curves which lie on this surface and which pass through the point A. (Generally speaking, it will not be their principal normal at this point.)

41

EXAMPLES. The normal to the surface of a sphere at any point is the radius of the sphere drawn to that point.

The normal to the surface of a cylinder at any point is the radius of the circular section of the cylinder at that point.

Note. A curve does not necessarily have a tangent at each of its points. Let us take, for example, a broken line; it is not possible to determine a tangent for it at one of its vertices. Similarly, a space curve does not necessarily have an osculating plane; nor a surface a tangent plane and a normal, and so on. For example, a conic surface has neither a tangent plane nor a normal at the vertex of the cone.

In all that follows we shall limit ourselves to *"smooth" curves*, that is, to curves which have at every point a tangent, an osculating plane, and a center of curvature, and to *smooth surfaces*, that is, to surfaces which have a normal at every point. On a surface, we shall consider only "smooth" curves.

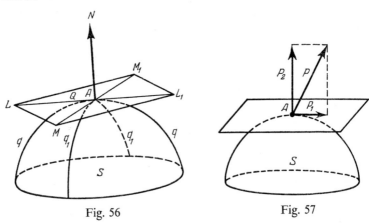

Fig. 56   Fig. 57

2. The condition of equilibrium of a point on a surface. Let us consider a point A which is able to move only along a surface S. Let P be a force acting on this point (Fig. 57). We shall denote by P_1 the tangential component of the force P (that is, the component which lies in the tangent plane Q to the surface S at point A), and by P_2 the normal component, which is directed along the normal to the surface S at the point A. The tangential component will move the point A along the surface; therefore, for the point A to be in equilibrium on the surface, the tangential component P_1 must be equal to zero. This means that the force P coincides with its normal

42

component P_2. Thus *for equilibrium of a point A on a surface, it is necessary that the resultant P of the forces acting on the point A be directed along the normal to the surface at this point.*

3. Some problems on the shortest lines in space. Find the shortest line which joins points of two space curves.

Repeating the argument of subsection 3 of Section 5, we find that the shortest line joining points of two curves is a common normal segment. In particular, the line which gives the shortest distance between points of two non-intersecting lines in space is the segment of a common perpendicular. Finally, it can be shown analogously that the shortest distance between two surfaces is the segment of a common normal.

3

GEODESIC PATHS

8. J. Bernoulli's Theorem on Geodesic Paths

1. Equilibrium of an elastic string on a surface. Suppose we are given two points A and B on some surface. These points can be joined by an infinite number of paths lying on the surface. Among these paths a shortest path q can be found. Our problem is to investigate the properties of this shortest path.

Imagine an elastic string stretched on the surface and secured at points A and B (Fig. 58). The string is in a state of equilibrium if

Fig. 58

it takes the form of the shortest path q. Indeed, if we pull it from position q, changing its form somewhat, then we lengthen it; and since the string tends to shorten itself, it will again assume the position q when we release it. Consequently, *a string lying along the shortest path q will be in a state of equilibrium and will therefore be stable.*

We begin with the investigation of curves of equilibrium of an elastic string on a surface.

Let us consider first of all a string $\overarc{AB}$ having the form of an arc of a circle (Fig. 59), and let $\overarc{CD}$ be a small section of it. Then the rest of the string exerts tensions on $\overarc{CD}$: the portion $\overarc{AC}$ will exert a tension at A, and the portion $\overarc{DB}$ will exert a tension at D. These tensions are directed along the tangents at points C and D. Let us denote them by P_1 and P_2. The forces P_1 and P_2 are equal in magnitude; otherwise the part $\overarc{CD}$ of our string would not remain in a state of equilibrium. Let us now find the resultant of the forces P_1 and P_2.

44

Let the tangents at C and D (along which the tensions P_1 and P_2 act) meet in the point M. Let us transfer the forces P_1 and P_2 to the point M. It is easy to see that the resultant will be directed toward the center O of the circle on which the string $\overarc{AB}$ is disposed. Denote the mid-point of the arc $\overarc{CD}$ by E. The resultant of the tensions acting on the arc $\overarc{CD}$ passes through the midpoint E of this arc and is directed along the radius EO. Because the radius EO is normal to the arc $\overarc{AB}$ at point E, we finally see that *the resultant of the*

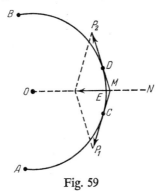

Fig. 59

tensions acting on an arc $\overarc{CD}$ of a circle passes through the center E of this arc and is directed along the normal to the circle at point E.

Let us now examine the general case. Suppose an elastic string is stretched between points A and B in the form of a curve q. Select a small piece $\overarc{CD}$ of this string.† On $\overarc{CD}$ the tensions P_1 and P_2 act at the points C and D and are directed along the tangents to q at these points. We can consider the small arc of our curve as an arc of the osculating circle at the midpoint E of this arc. The radius EO of this circle is directed along the *principal normal to the curve q at point E*. The resultant of the tensions acting on the arc of a circle acts along the radius which passes through the midpoint of this arc, in the given case along the radius EO. Thus *the resultant of the tensions acting on a small arc $\overarc{CD}$ of our string passes through its midpoint E and is directed along the principal normal EO at the point E.*

† In view of the smallness of AB we can consider it to be an arc of a circle and use the same Fig. 59.

It is not difficult now to find the conditions under which the string will be in equilibrium. If the string is in a state of equilibrium, then each small part $\overset{\frown}{CD}$ of it is also in a state of equilibrium. In order for the arc $\overset{\frown}{CD}$ to be in equilibrium, it is necessary that the resultant force on it to be directed along the normal to the surface. The tensions acting on $\overset{\frown}{CD}$ have a resultant directed along the principal normal EO to the curve q. Hence, one and the same straight line EO must be at the same time the principal normal to the curve q at the point E and the normal to the surface S at this point.

We obtain the following theorem: *In order for an elastic string q stretched on a surface S to be in a state of equilibrium, it is necessary that at any point A the principal normal coincide with the normal to the surface.*

2. Geodesic paths. *A path q is called a geodesic on a surface S if at each point of q the principal normal coincides with the normal to the surface.*

A geodesic path can also be defined as a path on a surface which has at every point an osculating plane passing through the normal to the surface at that point. In fact let A be a point on a curve q lying on a surface S. The normal to the surface at a point E is at the same time a normal to the curve q at this point; this normal will be the principal normal if it lies in the osculating plane to q at the point A.

The theorem given above can be formulated as follows: *A stretched string on a surface will be in a state of equilibrium if it is disposed along a geodesic curve of this surface.*

EXAMPLE 1. On the surface of a cylinder, stretched strings will arrange themselves, as we have found previously, along helices. *Helices are therefore geodesic curves on the surface of a cylinder.* The principal normals to helices coincide with the normals to the surface of the cylinder. The normals to the surface of a cylinder are the radii of circular sections. Thus *the principal normals to a helix are the radii of the circular sections of the cylinder on which it lies.*

EXAMPLE 2. Let us examine the conditions under which a plane curve q can be a geodesic curve on some surface S. Let us denote by Q the plane in which the curve q lies. For the plane curve q the osculating plane at each of its points will be the plane Q itself.

By the second definition of a geodesic curve, if the curve q is a geodesic curve, then the normals of the surface S at the points of the curve q must lie in its osculating plane, that is, the normals to the surface S at points of the curve q must lie in the plane Q.

EXAMPLE 3. Let us consider the surface of a sphere. Let us cut this surface by a plane Q which passes through the center of the sphere. In this way we obtain a so-called great circle on the surface of the sphere. *A great circle is a geodesic curve on the surface of a sphere.*

For the normal to the surface of a sphere at any point is the radius through that point. The radii at points of a great circle lie in the plane of this circle. We have a case of a plane curve on a surface at whose points the normals to the surface lie in the plane of this curve. But we have just seen that such a plane curve is a geodesic.

If we cut the sphere by a plane O_1 which does not pass through the center of the sphere, then we obtain a small circle on the surface of the sphere. Because normals to the surface of a sphere (that is, radii of the sphere) at points of a small circle do not lie in the plane of the small circle, a small circle is not a geodesic on the surface of a sphere.

An elastic string, tightly stretched along the arc of a great circle, will be in a state of equilibrium. If, however, the string is stretched along an arc of a small circle, then it will slide from this arc, because, lying along a path which is not a geodesic, it cannot be in equilibrium.

THEOREM OF JEAN BERNOULLI. *The shortest of all paths joining two points on a surface is an arc of a geodesic.*

We already have a proof of Bernoulli's theorem. In fact, on the one hand, we have proven that lines along which stretched strings on a surface are in equilibrium are geodesics. On the other hand, we know that an elastic string on a surface, held at points A and B on it and lying along the shortest path that joins these points, is in a state of equilibrium.

Note. Let us draw a great circle q through two points A and B on the surface of a sphere. The points A and B divide q into two arcs—the arc $\overparen{AMB}$ and the arc $\overparen{ANB}$ (Fig. 60). Both of these arcs are geodesics joining the points A and B. Let arc $\overparen{AMB}$ be shorter than arc $\overparen{ANB}$. Then, obviously, $\overparen{AMB}$ is the shortest arc on the surface of the sphere joining the points A and B; the arc $\overparen{ANB}$, although a geodesic, nevertheless will not be the shortest arc on the surface of the sphere joining the points A and B. An elastic string stretched on the surface of the sphere along either of these two arcs will be in a state of equilibrium. But whereas the string stretched along the arc $\overparen{AMB}$ is in a state of *stable* equilibrium, the string stretched along the arc $\overparen{ANB}$ is in a state of *unstable* equilibrium. If we displace the string from position $\overparen{ANB}$ so that it takes the form of a curve $\overparen{AN_1B}$ (Fig. 60), which is near to $\overparen{ANB}$ but is shorter, then it will slide along the surface of the sphere away from position $\overparen{ANB}$.

Thus we see that the *property of being a geodesic is a necessary, but not a sufficient, condition for a curve to be the shortest.*

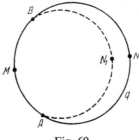

Fig. 60

It can be shown, however, that a sufficiently small arc of a geodesic is always the shortest path between its end points.

A geodesic curve can be defined as a path of which every sufficiently small arc is the shortest path between its end points.

3. "Construction" of a geodesic curve. Let us draw the edge of a knife along some surface S; at each instant the edge of the knife will touch the surface at some point A (Fig. 61). Let us hold the knife so that the

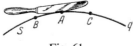

Fig. 61

normal to the surface at the point of contact with the edge of the knife always lies in the plane of the knife. The line q which is traced by the edge of the knife on the surface S will be a geodesic. To see this, let us consider a small arc $\overparen{BC}$ of the curve q traced by the knife and a point A on it. We can consider the arc $\overparen{BC}$ as situated approximately in the plane of the knife at the moment when the edge touches the surface at point A. In this way, the plane of the knife at the instant of contact of its sharp edge with the surface at point A is the osculating plane of the curve q at point A. But, from the preceding, we know that if the osculating plane of a curve q always passes through the normal to the surface, then the curve q is a geodesic. Consequently, the curve q is a geodesic on our surface.

One more problem for arbitrary surfaces can be considered: develop onto a plane a narrow strip cut from the surface, and, conversely, roll a plane strip onto a surface. It is necessary to define more exactly what we mean by this.

Let a curve q on a surface be given. Let us enclose it in a narrow strip (Fig. 62). This strip, generally speaking, cannot be developed onto a plane without distorting the lengths of curves lying in the strip. However, the narrower the strip the smaller will be the distortion.†

If we roll the narrow strip of the surface onto a plane, then the shortest curve on the strip joining two points becomes a curve which has the analogous property on the plane strip, that is, which is a segment of a straight line. Conversely, a straight line segment on a plane strip which is rolled onto a surface becomes a shortest arc on the surface—a geodesic

Fig. 62

arc. Therefore, a narrow strip (a ribbon, the width of which is very small compared to its length) which encloses a straight line segment *will lie on the surface so that the straight line segment becomes a geodesic arc.* Our narrow ribbon will lie on the surface along a geodesic curve. Therefore, by placing long narrow strips upon a surface, a representation of the paths of geodesic curves on the surface can be constructed.

9. Additional Observations on Geodesic Paths

1. The plane of symmetry. We now introduce some examples of geodesic curves. We first recall an important definition: *two points A and A' are symmetric with respect to a plane Q provided Q is the perpendicular bisector of the line segment joining A and A'* (Fig. 63).

Two figures q and q' are said to be symmetric with respect to a plane Q if, for each point A of the figure q, there is a corresponding point A' of the figure q' such that A and A' are symmetric with respect to Q, and vice versa (Fig. 64).

The plane Q is called a plane of symmetry of a surface S if it divides the surface S into two parts which are symmetric with respect to Q.

EXAMPLES. For the surface of a sphere, any plane that passes through the center of the sphere will be a plane of symmetry.

† Expressed in the language of the analysis of infinitesimals, changes in the lengths of the curves will be infinitesimals of a higher order than the width of the strip; cf. Section 14.

49

For surfaces of circular cones and cylinders, planes that contain the axes are planes of symmetry.

For finite circular cylinders, the plane that is the perpendicular bisector of the axis is a plane of symmetry.

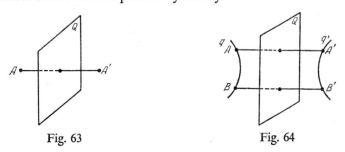

Fig. 63   Fig. 64

For an infinite cylinder (that is, for a cylinder whose generators are infinite straight lines), any plane perpendicular to the axis will be a plane of symmetry.

THEOREM. *If the plane Q is a plane of symmetry for the surface S, and if Q intersects the surface S along a curve q then q is a geodesic of the surface.†*

By definition, q lies in the plane Q. The plane curve q (see Example 2 in subsection 2 of Section 8) will be a geodesic if the

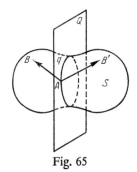

Fig. 65

normal to the surface S for every point of q lies in the plane Q. Let A be an arbitrary point of the curve q (Fig. 65). We shall show that the normal to the surface S at point A lies in the plane Q. Let us assume the contrary—that the normal AB to the surface S at point A does not lie in the plane Q. Let AB' be the straight line

† Remember that we are considering only smooth surfaces.

50

symmetrical to *AB* relative to *Q*. Because *AB* itself does not lie in *Q*, *AB* will differ from *AB'*. But the plane *Q* is a plane of symmetry for the surface, and if *AB* is normal to *S* at point *A*, then the line *AB'*, which is symmetrical to it, is also normal to *S* at point *A*. Thus the surface *S* possesses two normals at point *A*, which is not possible. We arrive at a contradiction; therefore we have shown that the normal *S* at any point *A* of the curve lies in the plane *Q*. Our theorem is proved.

2. Closed geodesics. If a loop of elastic string is stretched on a surface *S* so that it assumes a position of equilibrium, it will take

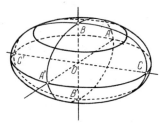

Fig. 66

the form of some closed path *q*. This path is a *geodesic curve* and is also *closed*. Thus an elastic loop on the surface of a sphere, if it takes the form of a great circle, will be in a state of equilibrium. Great circles on the surface of a sphere, and also ellipses—meridians on the surface of an ellipsoid of revolution—are closed geodesic curves (for surfaces of revolution, see Section 10).

If a closed surface *S* has several planes of symmetry, then *each plane of symmetry* intersects the surface along a closed geodesic, by virtue of the theorem proved above.

An ellipsoid with the three axes *AA'*, *BB'*, *CC'* of different lengths (Fig. 66) has three planes of symmetry, each of which passes through two axes of the ellipsoid. These three planes intersect the ellipsoid along three ellipses E_1, E_2, E_3—three closed geodesics.

It can be proved that *on any closed surface there are at least three closed geodesics.*†

† This is not an elementary theorem. Its proof is given in an article (in Russian) by L. A. Lyusternik and L. Shnirel'man, "Topological Methods in Variational Problems and their Application to Differential Geometry of Surfaces", *Uspekhi Matematicheskikh Nauk*, II, No. 1 (17), 1947.

3. Hertz's principle. A point moving in a plane with no external forces acting on it moves in a straight line (Newton's first law). *A point moving on a surface and on which no external forces act moves along a geodesic curve.* This is the substance of *Hertz's principle.* For example, a point on the surface of a sphere, if no external force acts upon it, moves along a great circle; on the surface of a cylinder, along a helix.

In fact, the acceleration which the point experiences in moving along a curve q can be resolved into a *tangential* component (directed along the tangent to q) and a *normal* component (directed along the principal normal to the curve q). But if the point moves without the action of external forces along a curve q situated on a surface S, then only the reaction of the surface acts on the point; the force of reaction of the surface is directed along the normal to the surface. Because the direction of a force coincides with the direction of the acceleration, the direction of the acceleration of our point must at every instant coincide with the direction of the normal to the surface. The normal to the surface at a point of the curve is perpendicular to the tangent to the curve q at the same point. Since the acceleration is directed along the normal to the surface, that is, perpendicular to the tangent q, the tangential acceleration equals zero. Consequently, our point has only normal acceleration, directed along the principal normal to q. The direction of the acceleration is at one and the same time the direction of the principal normal to the curve q and the direction of the normal to the surface S. Hence these directions coincide for any point of the curve q, from which it follows that the curve q is a geodesic on the surface S.

4. Geodesics on a surface with an edge. Let us consider a surface S consisting of two smooth surfaces S_1 and S_2 which adjoin one another along a curve s, which we shall call the *edge* of the surface S (for example, a dihedral angle would be such a surface). Let us take two points A and B, lying on S_1 and S_2, respectively (Fig. 67), and let $q_0 = \widehat{ACB}$ be a position of equilibrium of an elastic string on the surface S. Here C is a point on the edge s, and the arcs $\widehat{AC}$ and $\widehat{CB}$ of q_0 lie on the surfaces S_1 and S_2, respectively. Obviously, $\widehat{AC}$ is a geodesic on S_1 and $\widehat{CB}$ a geodesic on S_2. Let us find the condition for equilibrium at the point C on the edge by the method which we used in Section 8. The curve q_0 is the position of equilibrium of the flexible string on the surface S with end points fixed at points A and B.

Let α be the angle between the arc $\widehat{AC}$ and the part CC' of the edge s, and β the angle between the arc $\widehat{CB}$ and the part CC'' of the edge s. At point C there act tensions P_1, directed along the tangent to the arc CA, and P_2 directed along the tangent to the arc $\widehat{CB}$. Let the magnitude of each of these forces be T. Then the projections of the vectors representing these forces on the line LL_1 tangent to the edge s at C are vectors with magnitudes $T\cos\alpha$ and $T\cos\beta$, and the forces act in opposite directions. The condition for equilibrium

$$T\cos\alpha = T\cos\beta$$

gives us
$$\alpha = \beta, \tag{1}$$

so that the angles between the edge s and the arcs $\widehat{AC}$ and $\widehat{CB}$ are equal.

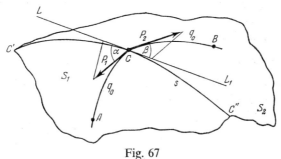

Fig. 67

It is natural to call the curve q_0 a *geodesic* on the surface S. If the surface S is composed of several smooth parts separated by edges

$$s_1, s_2, \ldots, s_n,$$

then the geodesic curves (lines of equilibrium of an elastic string) consist of arcs of geodesics which meet at the edges

$$s_1, s_2, \ldots, s_n,$$

and at each edge condition (1) is fulfilled.

Shortest paths on the surface S are geodesics. The property of shortest paths on surfaces made up of several plane "faces" (proved in Section 1) is a special case of the property of geodesics (shortest curves) on curved surfaces having several edges.

The property stated above for geodesics on curved surfaces with several edges can also be deduced from Hertz's principle.

10. Geodesic Paths on Surfaces of Revolution

1. Surfaces of revolution. Let us revolve a plane curve q around a straight line AB which lies in the same plane as q (Fig. 68). With the revolution of q around AB, a surface S is formed, which is called a surface of revolution. Any plane Q which passes through the axis of revolution AB intersects S along a pair of curves q and q'. These curves are called *meridians*. They are obtained from the curve q by

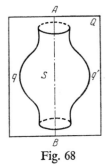

Fig. 68

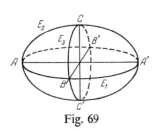

Fig. 69

turning it through a suitable angle around the axis of revolution. Every plane perpendicular to the axis intersects S along a circle called a *parallel*.

THEOREM 1. *All meridians of a surface of revolution are geodesic curves.*

In fact, let us consider the meridians q and q' formed by the intersection of the surface of revolution by a plane Q which passes through the axis AB. The plane Q is a plane of symmetry of the surface of revolution S; consequently, Q intersects the surface S along a geodesic curve. Thus q and q' are geodesics.

EXAMPLE. Let us revolve an ellipse E around its axis (Fig. 69). We obtain an *ellipsoid of revolution*. Its meridians are ellipses congruent to E. These ellipses are geodesics.

Remark. On the surface of a cylinder, all parallels are geodesics; on the surface of a sphere, of all the parallels only the equator is a geodesic; on the surface of a cone, none of the parallels is a geodesic.

2. Clairaut's theorem. Let us consider a geodesic curve q on a surface of revolution S. Let A be an arbitrary point of the geodesic q, r its distance from the axis of revolution (the radius of the parallel through A), α the angle between the geodesic q and the meridian at the point A.

THEOREM 2 (Clairaut). *At all points A of a geodesic q, the expression* $r \sin \alpha$ *has the same value:*

$$r \sin \alpha = c = \text{const.} \tag{1}$$

If we denote the angle between the geodesic and the parallel by β, then formula (1) assumes the form

$$r \cos \beta = \text{const.}$$

The special cases of Clairaut's theorem for conic surfaces and cylinders have already been proved (see subsection 4 of Section 3).

Let us consider a surface S_n formed by revolving a broken line $A_0 A_1 \ldots A_n$ around an axis L. The surface S_n consists of n surfaces $s_1, s_2, \ldots, s_n$ formed by revolution of the corresponding sides $A_0 A_1, A_1 A_2, \ldots, A_{n-1} A_n$. These surfaces are separated from each other by the "edges" $t_1, t_2, \ldots, t_{n-1}$—parallels obtained by revolving the vertices of the broken line $A_1 A_2 \ldots A_{n-1}$.

Consider two points A and B on the surface S_n and the geodesic q_0 which joins them. By virtue of the proof in subsection 4 of Section 9, the geodesic q_0 consists of geodesic arcs on the surfaces of truncated cones or cylinders

$$s_1, s_2, \ldots, s_n,$$

which meet at the edges

$$t_1, t_2, \ldots, t_{n-1},$$

and the angles formed by each of the edges t_i with the arcs of the geodesic on either side of it are equal. As one moves along q_0, the angle β of the curve q_0 with the parallel changes continuously, without jumps (a jump in the change of this angle could occur if the parallel became one of the edges; but by what has been said above, this does not happen). Therefore, the value of $r \cos \beta$ also changes continuously.

Let us watch what happens to the value $r \cos \beta$ as we move along q_0. As long as we move along one of the surfaces

$$s_0, s_1, \ldots, s_n,$$

the value of $r \cos \beta$ remains constant (by virtue of the special cases of Clairaut's theorem already proved). On crossing one of the edges

$$t_1, t_2, \ldots, t_{n-1},$$

the value of this expression does not change, by what we showed above (Section 9, subsection 4). Hence, it is constant along the

55

whole of the line q_0. Thus, for all points of a geodesic q_0, the relationship

$$r \cos \beta = \text{const.}$$

holds true.

An arbitrary plane curve m can be considered as the limit of inscribed broken lines m_n, when the number n of their sides grows indefinitely and the length of the greatest side approaches zero. A surface S, formed by the revolution of m around some axis, is the limit of the surfaces S_n which are formed by rotation of the broken lines m_n around the same axis. Now Clairaut's theorem holds for shortest paths on the surfaces S_n. From this we can conclude that it holds also for shortest paths on the surface S.

PART II

4

PROBLEMS CONNECTED WITH THE POTENTIAL ENERGY OF A STRETCHED STRING

11. Length-preserving Displacements of Curves

1. The potential energy of a flexible string. Let us assume that a flexible string has equal tension T at all its points and that this tension is preserved during changes in the length of the string. Let us determine the potential energy of the string.

Let $q = \overparen{ABC}$ be a smooth curve having length l and consisting of the arcs $\overparen{AB}$ of length l_0 and $\overparen{BC}$ of length $(l - l_0)$ (Fig. 70). Let

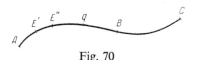

Fig. 70

a string occupying position $\overparen{AB}$ be stretched along the curve q to the position $\overparen{ABC}$, the end at the point A remaining fixed, and the end at the point B tracing out the curve $\overparen{BC}$ of length $(l - l_0)$. Let us consider the work done by the forces due to tension.

The forces due to tension at point B do work equal to $T(l - l_0)$.

The work of the forces of tension acting on a small arc $\overparen{E'E''}$ of the curve q equals zero. In fact, the resultant of these forces is directed along the normal to the curve q, whereas the arc $\overparen{E'E''}$ slides along the curve q itself.

57

Thus, the total amount of work done by the forces of tension during the movement of the string amounts to the work of the forces applied to the end B, that is, equals

$$T(l - l_0) = Tl - Tl_0.$$

Let the potential energy of the string when in the position $\overparen{AB}$ be V_0, and let its potential energy when in the position $\overparen{ABC}$ be V. The increase of potential energy $V - V_0$ equals the work done, so that

$$V - V_0 = Tl - Tl_0$$

or
$$V - Tl = V_0 - Tl_0. \tag{1}$$

We shall assume that as the length of the string approaches zero the potential energy approaches zero; consequently when $l_0 \to 0$ we have $V_0 \to 0$, and hence $(V_0 - Tl_0) \to 0$. Allowing l_0 to tend to zero in the right side of equality (1), we obtain in the limit

$$V - Tl = 0,$$

from which it follows that
$$V = Tl. \tag{2}$$

The potential energy of a flexible string is equal to its length multiplied by its tension.

Corollary. If during the displacement of a string the work done by the forces due to tension equals zero, then the length of the string does not change. In fact, under these conditions the potential energy of the string, which is proportional to the length of the string, does not change.

Let us note that if the straight line segment AB is displaced but still remains a straight line segment, then the total amount of work done by the forces of tension is just the work done by these forces on the ends of this segment. The work done on a string which retains the form of a broken line ACB amounts to the work done by the forces of tension at the ends A and B of the broken line and at its vertex C.

2. Parallel curves. Two curves with common normals are said to be *parallel*. The simplest examples of parallel curves are parallel straight lines and concentric circles.

Theorem 1. *Segments of common normals between parallel curves q and q_1 have equal lengths.*

Let the common normal AB to the curves q and q_1 be displaced from position A_0B_0 to position A_1B_1, remaining always a common normal to the given curves (Fig. 71).

The work done by the forces of tension during this displacement is zero. In fact, at the end A the tension is directed along the normal to the curve; therefore, during the displacement of this end along the curve q the work done by the tension is zero. Analogously, at the end B during the displacement along the curve q_1 the work done by the tension is zero. Thus, during our displacement of the common

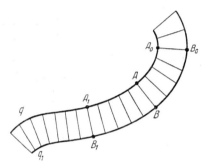

Fig. 71

normal the work done by tension is zero. From our last corollary it follows that the length l of the common normal does not change:

$$l(A_0B_0) = l(A_1B_1).$$

3. Normals to an ellipse and to a parabola. *The locus of all points B, the sum of whose distances from two given points F and F_1 is a constant, is called an ellipse:*

$$FB + F_1B = 2a \qquad (3)$$

(*a is some positive constant*).

The points F and F_1 are called the *foci* of the ellipse, the segments FB and F_1B radius vectors.

THEOREM 2. *The normal to an ellipse at any point B is the bisector BD of the angle FBF_1 formed by the radius vectors* (Fig. 72).

In fact, let an elastic string having the form of a broken line FBF_1 be held at points F and F_1; if this string is displaced by moving the point B along the ellipse, then its length (by virtue of (3)) does not change. Hence, no work is done by the forces of tension. The work

59

done by forces of tension amounts to the work done by the forces at the point B. At this point two equal forces are applied which act in the directions BF and BF_1. Their resultant P is directed along the bisector BD of the angle FBF_1. During the displacement of the point B along the ellipse, the work done by P is always zero; hence P must always be directed along the normal to the ellipse. It follows that the normal to the ellipse at any point B coincides with the bisector of the angle FBF_1.

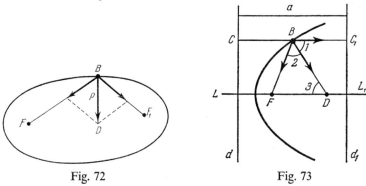

Fig. 72   Fig. 73

The locus of all points B, the distances of which from a given point F and from a given straight line d are equal,

$$FB = BC, \tag{4}$$

is called a parabola (BC is the perpendicular dropped from B to the straight line d (Fig. 73)).

The point F is called the *focus* of the parabola; the straight line d is the *directrix*; and the straight line LL_1, perpendicular to d and passing through the focus, is the *axis* of the parabola. Let us draw a straight line d_1 parallel to d so that the focus F and the directrix d are situated on the same side of d_1. Denote the distance between the parallel straight lines d and d_1 by a. Through the point B of the parabola let us draw the common perpendicular CC_1 to the straight lines d and d_1 (CC_1 is parallel to the axis LL_1). We have

$$CC_1 = CB + BC_1 = a,$$

where a is constant and equal to the distance between the parallel straight lines d and d_1. By virtue of (4),

$$FB + BC_1 = a. \tag{5}$$

It is not difficult now to prove the following assertion.

THEOREM 3. *The normal at an arbitrary point B of a parabola is the bisector of the angle FBC_1 formed by the radius vector FB and the straight line BC_1 parallel to the axis LL_1.*

Let us consider a string having the form of the broken line FBC_1, which has the end F fixed, while the end C_1 slides along the straight line d_1, so that BC_1 remains perpendicular to it and the point B slides along the parabola.

As is seen from formula (5), the length of this string remains unchanged as B moves along the parabola; hence the total work done by the forces of tension is zero. This work consists of the work done by tension at points C_1 and B. The work of the force of tension at the point C_1 is zero because the direction of this force (along the segment C_1B) is perpendicular to the straight line d_1 along which the point C_1 moves. Hence the work of the forces of tension at the point B is also zero. Repeating the arguments given in our discussion of the ellipse, we arrive at the proof of the theorem.†

Note. From Theorem 3 we obtain a method for constructing normals to a parabola. Let us mark off along the axis LL_1 a segment FD equal to the radius vector FB of the parabola. The straight line BD is the normal to the parabola.

Indeed, in Fig. 73, the angles $\angle 1$ and $\angle 3$ are equal because they are alternate interior angles of the parallels LL_1 and CC_1 and the transversal BD; the angles $\angle 3$ and $\angle 2$ are equal because the triangle FBD is isosceles. From this we see that $\angle 2 = \angle 1$, that is, BD is the bisector of the angle FBC; hence, by Theorem 3, BD is the normal to the parabola at point B.

4. Geodesic tangents and normals. If the geodesic arc $\overparen{AB}$ is displaced along a surface, then work is done only by the forces of tension which act at the ends A and B of the arc. Indeed, the resultant of the forces acting on any small internal part of the arc AB is directed along the normal to the surface, and hence its work during a displacement along the surface is zero.

By a *geodesic tangent* to a curve q on a surface at a point B is meant the geodesic curve r which has a common tangent with the curve q at point B; by a *geodesic normal* to a curve q at a point B

† Actually, we have proved this theorem for points situated on that part of the parabola which lies to the left of the straight line d_1. But, because the position of this line (parallel to d) is arbitrary, the theorem is true for all points of the parabola.

is meant the geodesic curve s orthogonal to q at point B (Fig. 74).

Theorem 1, which deals with common normals, can be generalized to the case of geodesic normals.

THEOREM 4. *Let two curves q and q_1 on a surface have all geodesic normals in common; then the segments of the common geodesic normals between q and q_1 have equal lengths* (Fig. 75).

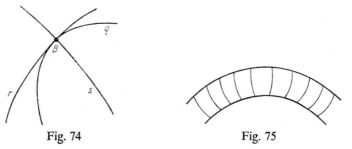

Fig. 74   Fig. 75

EXAMPLE. The segments of meridians on the surface of a sphere between two parallels have equal lengths.

The proof of Theorem 4 is a repetition of the proof of Theorem 1.

5. Geodesic circles. Given a point A on a surface and a positive number r, we mark off all the points B on the surface for which the length of the geodesic arc $\overset{\frown}{AB}$ equals r. The locus q of these points B is called a *geodesic circle*; the geodesic arcs AB are called *geodesic radii* (Fig. 76).

Fig. 76

At each point B of the geodesic circle q the geodesic normal is precisely the geodesic radius $\overset{\frown}{AB}$ of q.

In fact, let an elastic string $\overset{\frown}{AB}$, fastened at the end A and having the form of a geodesic radius, be displaced so that its end point B describes a geodesic circle q. Since the length of the geodesic arc $\overset{\frown}{AB}$

does not change, the work of the forces of tension is zero. This work amounts to the work of these forces at the end point B. This means that the tension in $\widehat{AB}$ must at each moment be perpendicular to the path taken by B. But this path is at each point in the direction of the tangent to q at B. Since the tension acts along $\widehat{AB}$, we see that $\widehat{AB}$ is perpendicular to the tangent to q at B, which is what we were to prove.

12. Evolutes and Involutes

Let us consider a plane curve q, a pencil of normals drawn from various points of this curve, and the *envelope* s of these normals (that is, the curve s tangent to these normals). The envelope s is

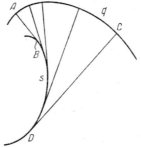

Fig. 77

called the *evolute* of the curve q, and the curve q, which is orthogonal to all the tangents to the curve s, is called an *involute* of the curve s (Fig. 77).

Each point B of the evolute is a point of intersection of the normal AB of the involute and a normal $A'B'$ "infinitely" close to it, that is, the point B is the center of curvature for the curve q at the point A (see Section 6). The evolute s of the curve q can be defined as the *locus of the centers of curvature of this curve.*

Let an elastic string have the form of a curve r which consists of the segment of the normal AB to the involute and the arc $\widehat{BD}$ of the evolute s (see Fig. 77). Moving along this curve from A to D, we have a *smooth* transition at the point B from the segment AB to the arc $\widehat{BD}$, since AB is tangent to s at B. Therefore, an elastic string in position $r = \widehat{ABD}$ is in a state of equilibrium. Let us displace the

63

string r so that its end point A moves along the involute, and the point B along the evolute; then AB maintains its position normal to the involute, but the remaining part of the string BD lies along the curve s. The work done by tension acting on the points of the normal AB is equal to its work at points A and B. But at point A this work is zero, because the tensions act along the normal to the curve q along which the end A slides. The tensions acting at point B are balanced and their work at any given instant equals zero. Finally, on the part $\overset{\frown}{BD}$ of the string r, which at any given instant does not take part in the movement, the work is zero. Thus, the

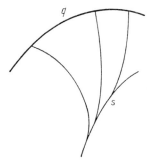

Fig. 78

work of the forces of tension at each instant is zero. During the time of our motion, the potential energy of the string r remains unchanged, and this means that the length of the string r also remains unchanged.

If $\overset{\frown}{ABD}$ is the initial position of the string r, and the segment CD its ultimate position, then the length of $\overset{\frown}{ABD}$ equals the length of CD:

$$l(\overset{\frown}{ABD}) = l(CD).$$

But $$l(\overset{\frown}{ABD}) = l(AB) + l(\overset{\frown}{BD})$$

or $$l(CD) = l(AB) + l(\overset{\frown}{BD}),$$

from which it follows that

$$l(\overset{\frown}{BD}) = l(CD) - l(AB).$$

We have proved the following theorem.

THEOREM. *If at two points A and C of an involute we draw normals AB and CD to their points of contact B and D with the evolute, then*

64

the difference in the lengths of these segments of the normals equals the length of the arc of the evolute $\overset{\frown}{BD}$ contained between them.

If to a curve q on a surface we draw a pencil of its geodesic normals (Fig. 78), then their envelope s is called the *geodesic evolute* of the curve q, and the curve q a *geodesic involute* of the curve s. The theorem remains true if the words "normals", "evolute", and "involute" are replaced by "geodesic normals", "geodesic evolute", and "geodesic involute". The reader can convince himself that the same proof applies in this case also.

13. Problems on the Equilibrium of a System of Elastic Strings

1. Dirichlet's principle. *For a mechanical system the position of its minimum potential energy is a position of equilibrium.* In fact, if a stationary mechanical system shifts from its position S of minimum potential energy, then its potential energy can only increase; and hence, according to the law of the conservation of energy, its kinetic energy can only decrease. Therefore, if the system was in a stationary state in position S, that is, had no kinetic energy, then upon displacement it cannot acquire positive kinetic energy, that is, it cannot start to move.

EXAMPLE. The potential energy of an elastic string is proportional to the length of the string. Therefore a position of equilibrium for the string is one in which its length is a minimum. We have already made repeated use of this fact.

Let us consider two problems concerned with finding the equilibrium position of a system of *several* strings (the second of these problems is important for our later work).

2. Problem of the minimum total length. Given points $B_1, B_2, \ldots, B_n$ in a plane, we are to find a point A_0 such that the sum of its distances from the given points is least. Let us consider n elastic strings $AB_1, AB_2, \ldots, AB_n$ which have one end A in common (for example, the strings are all joined at point A), the other ends being fixed at the points $B_1, B_2, \ldots, B_n$, respectively. The potential energy of our system of strings is proportional to the sum of the lengths of the strings $AB_1, AB_2, \ldots, AB_n$. The minimum total length of the strings, that is, the minimum potential energy, corresponds to the position of equilibrium of the system. In this position, each of the strings becomes a straight line segment, and the total length of these segments is a minimum. Let A_0 be the position of the point A in this position of equilibrium (Fig. 79). On A_0 there act n different forces, in the directions A_0B_1, A_0B_2, . . ., A_0B_n. These n forces cancel out. Thus at the point A_0 for which the sum of

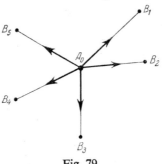

Fig. 79

the distances to the points B_1, B_2, . . ., B_n is a minimum, the resultant of the n equal forces acting in the directions A_0B_1, A_0B_2, . . ., A_0B_n is zero.†

Such a point A_0 can be found mechanically: on a horizontal sheet make n holes at the points B_1, B_2, . . ., B_n (Fig. 80); fasten

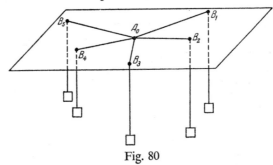

Fig. 80

† M. Ya. Vygodskii has pointed out that this proposition needs to be made more exact. It is true if the point A_0 for which the sum of the lengths AB_1, AB_2, . . ., AB_n is a minimum *does not coincide* with any of the points B_1, B_2, . . ., B_n.

Suppose, for example, we are given three points B_1, B_2, B_3. If none of the angles of the triangle B_1, B_2, B_3 exceeds 120°, then A_0 will lie inside this triangle. If, however, the angle at vertex B_1, say, of the triangle is greater than 120°, A_0 will coincide with B_1.

n strings at a single point above the sheet, pass these strings through the holes and hang equal weights on them. Our system of strings and weights will come to a state of equilibrium, and the common point of the strings in the state of equilibrium is the required point A_0. In fact, at this point n equal forces of tension act along the strings in the directions of the holes B_0, B_1, B_2, . . ., B_n (each of them equal to the weight of load hanging on the string). These n equal forces balance.

The following problem reduces to the one we have stated. Given n points B_1, B_2, . . ., B_n, suppose we are required to construct a store A and straight roads AB_1, AB_2, . . ., AB_n. We wish to find the position for A at which the cost of building the roads is a minimum, that is, at which the total length

$$AB_1 + AB_2 + . . . + AB_n$$

of road is a minimum.

Sometimes this problem is further complicated: let the freight movements from the store A to the points B_1, B_2, . . ., B_n be proportional to q_1, q_2, . . ., q_n, respectively. Select a position for the point A for which the sum

$$S = q_1 \overline{AB}_1 + q_2 \overline{AB}_2 + . . . + q_n \overline{AB}_n$$

will have its least value (that is, such that in the transfer of freight along the routes AB_1, AB_2, . . ., AB_n, the number of ton-kilometers will be a minimum).

The problem is solved in the same way as the previous problem (which is the special case where $q_1 = q_2 = . . . = q_n$). We wish to find the position of equilibrium of the system of n strings AB_1, AB_2, . . ., AB_n, which joins the points B_1, B_2, . . ., B_n to a common point A. But the strings AB_1, AB_2, . . ., AB_n have different tensions, proportional to the numbers q_1, q_2, . . ., q_n; say they are $q_1 T$, $q_2 T$, . . ., $q_n T$, respectively. The potential energies of the strings AB_1, AB_2 . . ., AB_n are $q_1 T \overline{AB}_1$, $q_2 T \overline{AB}_2$, . . ., $q_n T \overline{AB}_n$, respectively. The total potential energy of the system is

$$V = T(q_1 \overline{AB}_1 + q_2 \overline{AB}_2 + . . . + q_n \overline{AB}_n) = TS. \tag{1}$$

The position of the least value of V, that is, the least value of the sum S, is the position of equilibrium of the system. Each length AB_i ($i = 1, 2, . . ., n$) becomes a straight line segment. The common point $A = A_0$ of these strings is in a state of equilibrium under the action of the n tensions directed along the segments A_0B_1, A_0B_2, . . ., A_0B_n and proportional to the numbers q_1, q_2, . . ., q_n.

The mechanical method proposed above for finding the required point A_0 is still applicable; however, the loads fixed to the ends of the strings, which pass through the holes at the points B_1, B_2, . . ., B_n, must now be proportional to the numbers q_1, q_2, . . ., q_n.

3. A problem on the equilibrium of a system of two strings. Let us consider a non-homogeneous flexible string having the form $q = \widehat{ACB}$ (Fig. 81), with the ends A and B fixed and the point C

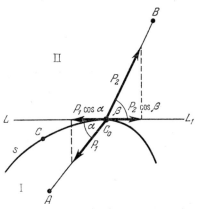

Fig. 81

moving along the curve s. We suppose that the tension is T_1, in the part $\widehat{AC}$ of the string, and T_2 in the part $\widehat{CB}$. The potential energy $V(q)$ of the string equals

$$V(q) = V(\widehat{AC}) + V(\widehat{CB}).$$

Since

$$V(\widehat{AC}) = T_1 l(\widehat{AC}),$$
$$V(\widehat{CB}) = T_2 l(\widehat{CB}),$$

we have
$$V(q) = T_1 l(\widehat{AC}) + T_2 l(\widehat{CB}). \qquad (2)$$

Let the string q have least potential energy in position q_0. By Dirichlet's principle, the string in position q_0 is in equilibrium. Let C_0 be the point of intersection of q_0 and s.

It is easy to see that each of the parts AC_0 and C_0B of the line q_0 is a straight line segment. Let us examine the conditions of equilibrium at point C_0. At this point there are applied the tension P_1, directed along C_0A, equal to T_1, and the tension P_2, directed along C_0B, equal to T_2. Let us draw the tangent LL_1 to the curve s at the point C_0. We shall use the notation

$$\left.\begin{array}{l} \angle AC_0L = \alpha, \\ \angle L_1C_0B = \beta. \end{array}\right\} \tag{3}$$

The tangential component of the force P_1 is $P_1 \cos \alpha = T_1 \cos \alpha$ and is directed along C_0L; the tangential component of the force P_2 is $P_2 \cos \beta = T_2 \cos \beta$ and is directed along C_0L_1. The point C_0 is in equilibrium if these tangential components cancel one another, that is, if

$$T_1 \cos \alpha = T_2 \cos \beta. \tag{4}$$

Thus the path q_0 is the broken line AC_0B, where the vertex point C_0 is the point on the curve s at which condition (4) is fulfilled.

5

THE ISOPERIMETRIC PROBLEM

14. Curvature and Geodesic Curvature

1. Curvature. Given a circle of radius R, we define its curvature to be the number $1/R$. Note that as the radius R increases, the curvature decreases.

Suppose we are given a circle with center O and radius R, and let $\overparen{AB}$ be an arc of this circle. Imagine that an elastic string is stretched along the arc $\overparen{AB}$, and let T_1 and T_2 be the forces of tension (directed along the tangents at the end points A and B) acting on the ends of the string; we assume that T_1 and T_2 have equal magnitudes (Fig. 82).

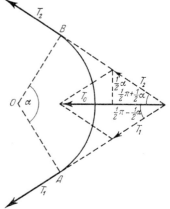

Fig. 82

The resultant T_0 of the forces T_1 and T_2 is directed along the bisector of the angle between the directions of the forces T_1 and T_2, that is, along the radius bisecting arc $\overparen{AB}$. If the radian measure of the angle AOB is α, then the length of the arc $\overparen{AB}$ is $R\alpha$, and the length of the chord joining A and B is $2R \sin \frac{1}{2}\alpha$. Since a very small arc of a circle has approximately the same length as its corresponding chord, the number $2R \sin \frac{1}{2}\alpha$ is, for very small values of α, very nearly equal to the number $R\alpha$. It follows that for very small values of α, $\sin \frac{1}{2}\alpha$ and $\frac{1}{2}\alpha$ are approximately equal; that is, small angles and their sines are, numerically speaking, approximately equal.

Note. More exactly, the quotient obtained by dividing the sine of an angle by the angle approaches 1 as the angle (measured in radians) approaches zero. Proof of this can be found in any book on mathematical analysis, and also in many trigonometry textbooks.

In order to make the arguments which follow more rigorous, we introduce the concept of *equivalent infinitesimals*. *By an infinitesimal we mean a variable which approaches zero.*

Let β approach zero along with α. (For example, in a circle the length of a chord approaches zero along with the length of the arc which it subtends.) If for values of α and β that approach zero the value of the fraction β/α also approaches zero, then we say that β is an *infinitesimal of a higher order* than α. For example, if α is any infinitesimal whatsoever, then α^2 is an infinitesimal of a higher order than α.

The infinitesimals α and γ are said to be *equivalent* provided their ratio approaches 1:

$$\lim_{\alpha \to 0} \frac{\gamma}{\alpha} = 1. \tag{1}$$

(In particular, we see that as γ approaches zero, so does α.) For example, in a circle the length of a chord and the length of the arc which the chord subtends are equivalent infinitesimals. If γ and α are equivalent infinitesimals, then their difference is an infinitesimal, and this difference is an infinitesimal of higher order than either γ or α. Indeed, from (1) it follows that

$$\lim_{\alpha \to 0} \frac{\gamma - \alpha}{\alpha} = 0. \tag{2}$$

Symbolically, we write $\alpha \approx \gamma$ when we wish to say that the infinitesimals α and γ are equivalent. It can be shown that

$$\lim_{\alpha \to 0} \frac{\sin \alpha}{\alpha} = 1,$$

so that $\sin \alpha$ and α (where α is measured in radians) are equivalent infinitesimals; using the notation which we have just introduced, we can write $\sin \alpha \approx \alpha$.

Finally, we note that (2) has the following useful interpretation: the error that results from substituting for an infinitesimal another infinitesimal, equivalent to the first, is an infinitesimal of higher order than either of those two.

Let α (measured in radians) denote the angle AOB (Fig. 82). Then the angle between the directions of the forces T_1 and T_2 is $\pi - \alpha$, and the angle between their directions and the direction of the resultant T_0 is $\frac{1}{2}\pi - \frac{1}{2}\alpha$. From the figure we see that $T_0 = 2T \sin \frac{1}{2}\alpha$, where T is the magnitude of the forces T_1 and T_2. If we denote the length of the arc $\overset{\frown}{AB}$ by s, then we have $\alpha = s/R$. Consequently,

$$T_0 = 2T \sin \frac{s}{2R}.$$

If the arc s is very small, then

$$\sin \frac{s}{2R} \approx \frac{s}{2R}$$

and

$$T_0 \approx T \frac{s}{R}.$$

Let us now consider an arbitrary curve q. If A is a point of q, and if we have an arc containing A and having a very small length s, then this arc can be thought of as approximating an arc of a circle of radius R, where R is the radius of curvature of the curve q at the point A. Let us imagine that q is an elastic string along which there is acting a tension T. Then at the ends of our small arc there act two forces due to the tension in the string. By the argument given above, the resultant of these two forces is directed along the radius of the circle of curvature and is equal (to be precise, is equivalent) to $T(s/R)$. *The number $1/R$ is called the curvature of the curve q at the point A.* Thus, *tension forces acting on a small arc $\overset{\frown}{AB}$ act in the direction of the principal normal; the resultant is proportional to the length of the arc $\overset{\frown}{AB}$ and to the curvature $1/R$ of the curve q at the point A.*

2. Geodesic curvature. Let us consider (Fig. 83) a small arc of length s of a curve q which lies on a surface, and let A be the mid-point of this arc. We shall denote the curvature of the curve at the point A by $1/R$, and the angle between the principal normal AN to q at A and the normal AN_1 to the surface by φ. A force directed along the principal normal to the curve q at point A acts on the small arc at the point A; the magnitude of this force is $T(s/R)$. We resolve this force into two forces: one acting along the normal to the surface and the other tangential to the surface. The component that acts along the normal is canceled by the reaction of the surface; the tangential component causes the arc to slide along the surface. The magnitude of the tangential force is (equivalent to)

$$\frac{Ts \sin \varphi}{R} = Ts\Gamma.$$

The number $\Gamma = (\sin \varphi)/R$ is called the *geodesic curvature* of the curve q at the point A. This number gives an indication of the magnitude of the force that acts on the arc of the string at point A, compelling the arc to slide along the surface. The force acting on a small arc of the curve is proportional to the length s of the arc and to the geodesic curvature Γ at a point on it.

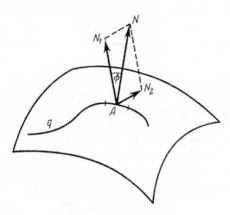

Fig. 83

For a geodesic curve we have $\varphi = 0$, and its geodesic curvature is zero. There will be no forces acting along a geodesic curve compelling an arc of the curve to slide along the surface (that is, a stretched string lying along a geodesic is in a state of equilibrium).

15. The Isoperimetric Problem

1. Measurement of the length of an arc of a circle. Let a circle q of radius R and an arc $\overset{\frown}{AB}$ of this circle be given. Let $\underset{\frown}{AB}$ be an arc close to the latter.† Let us denote the length of the arc $\overset{\frown}{AB}$ by l, the length of the arc $\underset{\frown}{AB}$ by $l + \Delta l$. If we transform the arc $\overset{\frown}{AB}$ so that it becomes the arc $\underset{\frown}{AB}$, then its length l increases by Δl, and therefore its potential energy increases by $T \cdot \Delta l$. Let us transform $\overset{\frown}{AB}$ into $\underset{\frown}{AB}$ so that each of its points C is displaced along a radius (Fig. 84). Let a very small arc $\overset{\frown}{CD}$ (part of $\overset{\frown}{AB}$) change into the

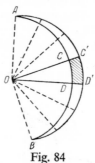

Fig. 84

small arc $\overset{\frown}{C'D'}$ (part of $\underset{\frown}{AB}$). Each point of this arc is displaced by a segment CC' (due to the smallness of $\overset{\frown}{CD}$, we consider the displacement of each of its points to be approximately the same). The small area $CC'D'D$, bounded by our arcs and by the segments CC' and DD', can be considered to be approximately a rectangle, and, if h is the length of the small arc $\overset{\frown}{CD}$, then the area of $CC'D'D$ is approximately equal (that is, equivalent) to hCC':

$$\text{area } CC'D'D \approx hCC'. \tag{1}$$

Let us note that on the arc $\overset{\frown}{CD}$ there acts a force directed along the radius and equal to Th/R, where R is the radius of our circle. The work we do in displacing the arc $\overset{\frown}{CD}$ until it coincides with $\overset{\frown}{C'D'}$ equals the force Th/R multiplied by the path CC', that is, $(Th/R)CC'$, or (see (1))

$$\frac{Th}{R} CC' = \frac{T}{R} \text{ (an area } CC'D'D). \tag{2}$$

† We assume, when speaking of the closeness of the new arc to the arc of the old circle, that points of the new arc are close to points of the old arc and the curvature of the new arc approximates the curvature of the old arc.

74

Thus *the work that must be performed for the displacement of a small arc $\overset{\frown}{CD}$ to a new, nearby position $\overset{\frown}{C'D'}$ is equal (more accurately, equivalent) to T/R multiplied by the area of the portion $CC'D'D$ of the surface which this arc sweeps out during its displacement.*

Let us denote the area of the part of the surface between the arcs $\overset{\frown}{AB}$ and $\underset{\frown}{AB}$ by ΔF. Divide this area into smaller areas (of the same type as $\overset{\frown}{CC'D'D}$) by means of radii originating from the center O. Then the arc $\overset{\frown}{AB}$ is divided into small arcs. In the course of its displacement each small arc $\overset{\frown}{CD}$ sweeps out an area $CC'D'D$. The work done in moving one of the small arcs is the product of T/R and the area swept out by the arc. The total work done in moving the large arc $\overset{\frown}{AB}$ is the sum of the amounts of work done in moving the small arcs, that is, T/R multiplied by the sum of the areas swept out by the small arcs, or $(T/R)\Delta F$, where ΔF is the area swept out by the arc $\overset{\frown}{AB}$ in the course of its displacement.

But the work done in moving $\overset{\frown}{AB}$ is also equal to the increase ΔV of potential energy during the change of the arc $\overset{\frown}{AB}$ into the arc $\underset{\frown}{AB}$:

$$\Delta V \approx \frac{T}{R} \Delta F. \tag{3}$$

On the other hand, from formula (2) of Section 11 it follows that

$$\Delta V = T \cdot \Delta l, \tag{4}$$

where Δl is the increase in the length of the arc.

Comparing (3) and (4), we obtain

$$\frac{T}{R} \Delta F \approx T \cdot \Delta l$$

or
$$\Delta l = \frac{1}{R} \Delta F. \tag{5}$$

The increase Δl in the length of the arc $\overset{\frown}{AB}$ is equal (more exactly, equivalent) to the curvature $1/R$ multiplied by the area of the region between the arcs $\overset{\frown}{AB}$ and $\underset{\frown}{AB}$.†

† All are equalities with an accuracy up to a higher order of smallness than Δl.

2. Change of the length of an arc of an arbitrary curve. If instead of a circle we take an arbitrary curve, then a small arc $\stackrel{\frown}{AB}$ of it can be considered to be an arc of a circle of radius R (R is the radius of curvature), and formula (5) is still applicable, if the curvature of the curve at the midpoint of the arc $\stackrel{\frown}{AB}$ is $1/R$.

The situation for curves on a surface is completely analogous, except that in this case the geodesic curvature is used instead of the curvature throughout. Formula (5) becomes

$$\Delta l = \Gamma \cdot \Delta F, \tag{6}$$

where Γ is the geodesic curvature, Δl the increase of the length of the arc of the curve upon its replacement by a nearby arc on the same surface, and ΔF the area lying between the initial and the terminal arcs.

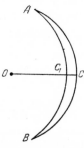

Fig. 85

In Fig. 84 the area ΔF lies *outside* the circle of which $\stackrel{\frown}{AB}$ is an arc. In Fig. 85 it is situated *inside* the circle. In the latter case, we shall consider the area ΔF to be negative. The increase Δl of the length of the arc of the circle is also negative (the arc has not been lengthened, but shortened).

3. The isoperimetric problem. Let us consider the following problem. *Of all the closed plane curves that enclose a given area F, find the one that has the least length.*

We assume that such a curve exists. Let us prove that it is a circle.

Let us note that a curve of constant curvature (that is, a curve having the same curvature $1/R$ at all of its points) is a circle.

We shall prove this fact, although we do not claim that our proof is by any means rigorous.

76

A very small arc of a curve whose curvature $1/R$ is constant can be considered as an arc of a circle of radius R. Let us think of the whole curve as consisting of a very large number of such small arcs, with neighboring arcs partially overlapping one another. Two partially overlapping small arcs of a circle form a new arc of the same circle. Thus, each adjacent pair of the small arcs comprising the curve form an arc of a circle of radius R. Continuing this argument we find that each 3, 4, 5, . . ., consecutive small arcs form an arc of a circle of radius R; consequently, the whole curve is an arc of a circle of radius R. Hence a closed curve having constant curvature $1/R$ is simply a circle of radius R.

Let q be a closed curve enclosing a region of area F, and assume the length of q is minimal. Let us suppose that q is not a circle; that is, let us suppose that q does not have constant curvature.

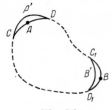

Fig. 86

If q does not have constant curvature, then there are two points A and B of q (Fig. 86) where the curvature is not the same; thus, denoting the curvature of q at A and at B by

$$\frac{1}{R_1} \quad \text{and} \quad \frac{1}{R_2}, \quad \text{respectively,}$$

we have $$R_1 \neq R_2.$$

For definiteness, let us assume

$$\frac{1}{R_1} < \frac{1}{R_2}.$$

Let $\widehat{CD}$ and $\widehat{C_1 D_1}$ be two small arcs of the curve q; assume these arcs contain the points A and B respectively. Let us substitute a nearby arc $\widehat{CA'D}$ for the arc $\widehat{CD}$, and a nearby arc $\widehat{C_1 B' D_1}$ for the arc $\widehat{C_1 D_1}$. Denote by ΔF_1 the area enclosed by $\widehat{CD}$ and $\widehat{CA'D}$, and by ΔF_2 the area enclosed by $\overset{\frown}{C_1 D_1}$ and $\overset{\frown}{C_1 B' D_1}$. By formula (5), substitution of the arc $\overset{\frown}{CA'D}$ for the arc $\overset{\frown}{CD}$ changes the length of the curve q, by a quantity equal (more exactly, equivalent) to $(1/R_1)\Delta F_1$, while substitution of the arc $\overset{\frown}{C_1 B' D_1}$ for the arc $\overset{\frown}{C_1 D_1}$ increases the length of q by $(1/R_2)\Delta F_2$. The area of the region enclosed by q is increased by $\Delta F_1 + \Delta F_2$, and the total increase in the length of q is (equivalent to)

$$\frac{1}{R_1}\Delta F_1 + \frac{1}{R_2}\Delta F_2.$$

Let us now choose the arcs $CA'D$ and $C_1 B' D_1$ so that ΔF_1 and ΔF_2 are equal in absolute value but opposite in sign, and such that $\Delta F_1 > 0$. Then $\Delta F_2 = -\Delta F_1 < 0$, and the increase in area is $\Delta F_1 + \Delta F_2 = 0$—in other words, changing the shape of the curve q has not changed the area of the region it encloses. The increase in the length of q is (equivalent to)

$$\Delta F_1 \left(\frac{1}{R_1} - \frac{1}{R_2} \right);$$

and since

$$\frac{1}{R_1} < \frac{1}{R_2},$$

we have

$$\Delta F_1 \left(\frac{1}{R_1} - \frac{1}{R_2} \right) < 0.$$

Thus the increase in the length of q is negative, so that the curve q is transformed into a shorter curve q_1 which encloses a region of the same area F. Hence, of all those curves which enclose regions of area F, q is not the one of least length. This contradicts our original assumption regarding q.

Hence *the curve of least length among all curves that enclose a given area is a circle.*†

4. The isoperimetric problem for surfaces. Analogous problems can be considered for surfaces, only here the geodesic curvature $\Gamma = \dfrac{\sin \varphi}{R}$ plays the role of curvature throughout. For example, if

† A number of other proofs of the isoperimetric properties of circles are given in D. A. Kryzhanovskii's book, *Isoperimetry* (Boston: D. C. Heath and Company; to appear).

a small arc $\stackrel{\frown}{CD}$ of a curve q with geodesic curvature $\Gamma = \dfrac{\sin \varphi}{R}$ is replaced by a nearby arc $\stackrel{\frown}{CA'D}$, and if the area of the figure bounded by $\stackrel{\frown}{CD}$ and $\stackrel{\frown}{CA'D}$ is ΔF, then the resulting increase Δl in length is given by

$$\Delta l = \Delta F \frac{\sin \varphi}{R} = \Gamma \cdot \Delta F.$$

Repeating the proof of the preceding theorem, but substituting geodesic curvature for curvature throughout, we obtain a proof for the following theorem.

Among all closed curves on a surface that enclose a given area, a curve of constant geodesic curvature has the least length. (On a sphere such lines are great circles and small circles.)

Note. On spheres and planes, the curves of constant geodesic curvature are geodesic circles. On other surfaces, however, the curves of constant geodesic curvature are not generally geodesic circles.

6

FERMAT'S PRINCIPLE AND ITS CONSEQUENCES

16. Fermat's Principle

1. Fermat's principle. The problems we have been considering are very similar to the problems of geometric optics connected with the so-called *Fermat principle*.

We consider a plane optical medium, at every point $A(x, y)$ of which the velocity of light is given by a function $v = v(x, y) = v(A)$. The medium is said to be *homogeneous* if the velocity of light is the same at all points of the medium.

The time $T(q)$ required for a beam of light to traverse a path q is called the *optical length* of the curve q. It will of course depend in general on the parts of the medium through which q passes.

In a homogeneous optical medium in which the velocity of light is v, the optical length $T(q)$ of the path q is proportional to its physical length $l(q)$ and is given by the equation

$$T(q) = \frac{1}{v} \, l(q).$$

FERMAT'S PRINCIPLE. *In an optical medium, the path of light from a point A to a point B has the least optical length of all paths joining A and B.*

It follows that *in a homogeneous optical medium light is propagated along straight lines.*

2. The law of reflection. In a homogeneous optical medium a curve s is given (Fig. 87) which reflects light rays (that is, the curve s acts as a mirror). We wish to determine the path q_0 along which light travels from a point A to a point B after reflection in s. The path q_0 is the shortest of the paths q which join A and B, reflecting from s. Hence, this path (see Section 5) is the broken line ACB, where C is on the curve s, and where the line CD that bisects the angle ACB is the normal to the curve s at point C.

The angles $\alpha = ACD$ and $\beta = DCB$ formed by the half-lines AC and CB with the normal CD are called, respectively, the *angle of incidence* and the *angle of reflection*. Thus we arrive at Descartes' law of reflection of light: *for a beam of reflected light the angle of incidence is equal to the angle of reflection*.

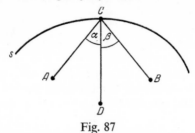

Fig. 87

From the properties of normals to an ellipse and to a parabola (proved in Section 11) we have the following:

If the curve s is an ellipse, then half-lines originating at a focus, upon reflection, converge to the other focus (Fig. 88).

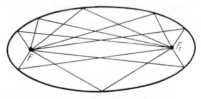

Fig. 88

If the curve s is a parabola, then half-lines originating at the focus of the parabola, upon reflection, form half-lines parallel to the axis of the parabola; conversely, half-lines parallel to the axis of the parabola, upon reflection, converge to the focus of the parabola (Fig. 89).

It is this property of parabolas which explains why the reflectors for searchlights, reflecting telescopes, etc., are made in the form of paraboloids of revolution. (A paraboloid of revolution is the surface obtained when a parabola is revolved about its axis.)

3. The law of refraction. Let us consider two homogeneous optical media I and II separated by a curve s (see Fig. 81); let v_1 be the velocity of light in medium I, and v_2 its velocity in medium II. We shall determine the path $q_0 = \widehat{AB}$ along which a beam of light travels in passing from point A in medium I to point B in medium II.

Let q be an arbitrary path joining the points A and B. If C is the point in which q intersects the boundary curve s between the two media, then q is composed of two arcs $\widehat{AC}$ and $\widehat{CB}$, lying in media I and II respectively. It follows that the optical length $T(q)$ of the curve q is given by

$$T(q) = T(\widehat{AC}) + T(\widehat{CB}) = \frac{l(\widehat{AC})}{v_1} + \frac{l(\widehat{CB})}{v_2}. \tag{1}$$

The path q_0 is the path of least optical length among all the paths q.

Let us also consider a non-homogeneous flexible string q held at points A and B, and suppose that a point C between A and B slides

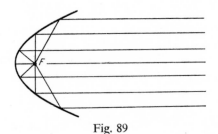

Fig. 89

along the curve s. Suppose that the tension in the part $\widehat{AC}$ of the string is $T_1 = 1/v_1$, and that the tension in part $\widehat{CB}$ is $T_2 = 1/v_2$.

By virtue of equation (2), Section 13, the potential energy $V(q)$ of the string is

$$V(q) = \frac{l(\widehat{AC})}{v_1} + \frac{l(\widehat{CB})}{v_2}. \tag{2}$$

Comparing formulas (1) and (2), we obtain

$$T(q) = V(q).$$

Thus the potential energy of the string q is numerically equal to the optical length of q. Hence the path q_0 of least optical length is also the curve along which a stretched string has the least potential energy.

By formula (4), Section 13, q_0 is the broken line AC_0B. Let α and β be the angles formed by the segments AC_0 and C_0B with the

82

line LL_1 which is tangent to the curve s at the point C. From formula (4), Section 13, it follows that

$$\frac{\cos \alpha}{v_1} = \frac{\cos \beta}{v_2}. \tag{3}$$

This last equation is the mathematical formulation of a law of optics known as the *law of refraction of light*. If the complements of the angles α and β are α_1 and β_1 (the angles which the segments AC_0 and C_0B make with the normal to the curve s at point C_0), then formula (3) can be written in the form

$$\frac{\sin \alpha_1}{v_1} = \frac{\sin \beta_1}{v_2}.$$

The angle α_1 is called the *angle of incidence*, and β_1 is called the *angle of refraction*.

17. The Curve of Refraction

1. The simplest case. Suppose the coordinate plane is divided into strips by a series of straight lines parallel to the x-axis, and suppose

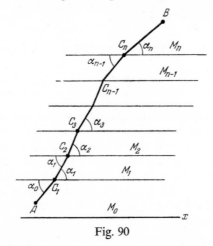

Fig. 90

that in each of these strips the velocity of light is constant (Fig. 90). Let us choose two points A and B from two different strips M_0 and M_n. Lying between the strips M_0 and M_n are strips M_1, M_2, . . ., M_{n-1}. Let the velocity of light in M_0 be v_0, in M_1 be v_1, in M_2 be

v_2, and so on. The path of a ray of light traveling from point A to point B is a broken line $AC_1C_2 \ldots C_nB$, where the successive vertices of the broken line are points lying on the lines dividing successive strips. Let the angles between the sides AC_1, C_1C_2, C_2C_3, . . ., $C_{n-2}C_{n-1}$, $C_{n-1}C_n$, C_nB of this broken line and the corresponding dividing lines between the strips be denoted by α_0, α_1, α_2, . . ., α_{n-1}, α_n, respectively. At the point C_1 we have, by the law of refraction,

$$\frac{\cos \alpha_0}{v_0} = \frac{\cos \alpha_1}{v_1};$$

at point C_2,

$$\frac{\cos \alpha_1}{v_1} = \frac{\cos \alpha_2}{v_2};$$

and so on; finally, at point C_n,

$$\frac{\cos \alpha_{n-1}}{v_{n-1}} = \frac{\cos \alpha_n}{v_n}.$$

It follows that

$$\frac{\cos \alpha_0}{v_0} = \frac{\cos \alpha_1}{v_1} = \frac{\cos \alpha_2}{v_2} = \ldots = \frac{\cos \alpha_{n-1}}{v_{n-1}} = \frac{\cos \alpha_n}{v_n}. \quad (1)$$

Let us denote the common value of all these fractions by c; then in general we have

$$\frac{\cos \alpha}{v} = c, \quad (2)$$

where α is the angle of inclination of a side of the broken line to the x-axis, and v the velocity along this side.

The line tangent to the broken line at a point on any one of its sides is just the straight line of which that side is a segment. Therefore we can think of α in equation (2) as being the angle of inclination (with respect to the x-axis) of the line tangent to the broken line at a point of the broken line, and of v as the velocity of light at the point of tangency.

2. The curve of refraction. Let us consider an optical medium in which the velocity of light at points of the medium is a function of the y-coordinates of the points:

$$v = v(y),$$

where v is a continuous function of y. *The path q of a ray of light passing through such a medium is a curve such that*

$$\frac{\cos \alpha}{v} = c, \qquad (3)$$

where v is the velocity of light at an arbitrary point C of the curve q (Fig. 91), α is the angle between the tangent to the curve q at the point C and the x-axis, and c a constant that is not dependent upon our choice of the point C on the curve.

To establish equation (3) let us divide the medium into narrow strips of width h and consider that in each strip the velocity of light is a constant and equal to the velocity of light at the center of the strip (Fig. 91). Then, by virtue of the previous argument, the path

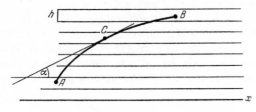

Fig. 91

of light from point A to point B will be a broken line $(AB)_h$ with vertices on the dividing lines between the strips; moreover, the condition stated in equation (3) is satisfied by the broken line $(AB)_h$. We have altered the distribution of the velocities somewhat, but this distribution approaches the original distribution more closely if we make the strips narrower.

Upon passing to the limit, letting the width h of the strips approach zero, we obtain our original continuous distribution of velocities of light. Then the broken lines $(AB)_h$ approach the curve q, for which condition (3) will also be satisfied.

3. Poincaré's model of the geometry of Lobachevskii. We shall consider the half-plane lying above the x-axis as an optical medium in which the speed of light is equal to the y-coordinate:

$$v = y.$$

Rays of light in such a medium will be semicircles with centers at points on the x-axis (Fig. 92).

85

In fact, let us consider one such semicircle q with its center at a point O on the x-axis. Let the y-coordinate of the point A of the semicircle be y, and let the angle ACO between the tangent line drawn at point A and the x-axis be the angle α. If R is the radius of the circle, then

$$y = R \sin \beta,$$

where

$$\beta = \angle AOC = \frac{\pi}{2} - \alpha;$$

or

$$y = R \cos \alpha,$$

i.e.

$$\frac{\cos \alpha}{y} = \frac{1}{R}.$$

Thus, the coordinates of any point on the semicircle q satisfy equation (3), that is, the equation for the ray of light in our medium. As we approach the x-axis, the velocity tends to zero.

It can be proved that the part AD of the semicircle q, one end of which lies on the x-axis, has infinite optical length. Points on the x-axis are therefore called "*infinitely remote points*".

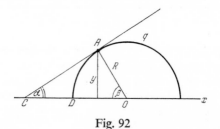

Fig. 92

Let us consider a semicircle having its center on the x-axis to be a "*straight line*", the optical lengths of the arcs of such semicircles to be their "*lengths*", the angles at the point of intersection of such semicircles (angles between their tangents) to be their "*angles*" of intersection.

We obtain a geometry in which many of the propositions of ordinary geometry remain valid. Thus, through two points we can draw one and only one "straight line" (through two points on a half-plane only one semicircle can be drawn with center on the x-axis). A "segment" has the least "length" of all lines joining its ends. Two straight lines having a common "*point at infinity*" (that is, two semicircles which touch one another at the x-axis on which their centers lie) are naturally considered to be "parallel".

Through a given point A not lying on a "straight line" q one can draw two "straight lines" q_1 and q_2, parallel to q (Fig. 93). These straight lines divide the half-plane into four "quadrants" at the vertex A. Straight lines s_1 which pass through A and lie in the first

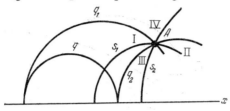

Fig. 93

pair of vertically opposite angles I and II intersect the "straight line" q. All the straight lines s_2 which lie in angles III and IV do not intersect q.

We thus obtain a representation of the geometry of Lobachevskii on a plane, the so-called Poincaré model for this geometry.

18. The Brachistochrone Problem

1. The cycloid. Let a circle K of radius R roll along a straight line LL_1; let us take the line LL_1 as the x-axis for a rectangular coordinate system (Fig. 94). The motion of the circle can be treated as a combination of two simpler motions that take place simultaneously: (1) rotation around the center O with an angular velocity ω; the linear velocity of points of the circle is $v = R\omega$; (2) a translational motion parallel to the x-axis at this same speed v. As the circle rolls along the x-axis, a point A on the circle traces out a curve called a *cycloid*.

At the instant $t_0 = 0$, let the point A be situated on the x-axis (see Fig. 94). At a later time t, the circle will have turned through an angle $\beta = t\omega$. The y-coordinate of the point A at this instant is

$$y = R(1 - \cos \beta) = 2R \sin^2 \frac{\beta}{2}. \tag{1}$$

Let us determine the direction of the velocity of point A at this instant. It will be in a direction tangential to the cycloid.

The velocity $T_1 = AD_1$ of the translational motion has magnitude v and is directed parallel to the x-axis and in the positive direction. The velocity $T_2 = AD_2$ of the motion around the center of the circle also has magnitude v and is directed along the tangent to the circle. The angle D_1AD_2 equals $(\pi - \beta)$. By adding these velocities according to the parallelogram law, we find the velocity of point A

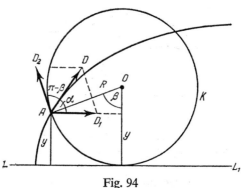

Fig. 94

along the cycloid. The velocity is directed along the bisector of the angle D_1AD_2 and forms the angle

$$\frac{1}{2}(\pi - \beta) = \frac{\pi}{2} - \frac{\beta}{2}$$

with the positive half of the x-axis (see Fig. 91). Thus, the angle α between the tangent to the cycloid at point A and the x-axis is

$$\alpha = \frac{\pi}{2} - \frac{\beta}{2}.$$

Therefore

$$\cos \alpha = \sin \frac{\beta}{2}. \tag{2}$$

From formulas (1) and (2) it follows that

$$\cos \alpha = \sqrt{\frac{y}{2R}}$$

or

$$\frac{\cos \alpha}{\sqrt{y}} = c. \tag{3}$$

88

Equation (3) relates the angle α, that is, the angle of inclination of the tangent to the cycloid at the point A, to the y-coordinate of A. Conversely, the locus of all those points which satisfy this equation is a cycloid.

2. The brachistochrone problem. Let A and B be two points, and suppose B lies below A (Fig. 95).

Let us join points A and B by a curve q; a point sliding from rest at A down to point B along q under the action of gravity will traverse the curve q in some interval of time, and the length of this time interval is called the *time of descent* along the curve q.

Find the curve q of quickest descent (in Greek, *brachistochrone*) which joins the points A and B, that is, the curve for which the time of descent from A to B is least.

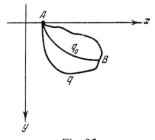

Fig. 95

First of all we set up a rectangular coordinate system in the vertical plane determined by points A and B, taking the x-axis to be the horizontal line passing through the point A, and the y-axis to be the vertical line through A. We take the downward direction to be the positive direction on the y-axis; we choose for the positive half of the x-axis that half lying on the same side of the y-axis as the point B. Let a point be in a state of rest at A, and suppose it begins to slide under the action of gravity. The velocity of the point at any time is related to its y-coordinate by the equation

$$v^2 = 2gy$$

or
$$v = \sqrt{2g} \cdot \sqrt{y}. \tag{4}$$

Let us imagine that we have an optical medium in which the velocity of light v is given by formula (4); then the optical length of the curve q is numerically equal to the time of descent along this curve. Let q_0 be that path (in the vertical coordinate plane) from A to B having the smallest possible optical length. The path q_0 coincides with the brachistochrone joining A and B.

For the curve q_0 the following equality is fulfilled (see equation (3), Section 17):

$$\frac{\cos \alpha}{v} = \frac{\cos \alpha}{\sqrt{2g} \cdot \sqrt{y}} = c \ (c \text{ is a const.})$$

or
$$\frac{\cos \alpha}{\sqrt{y}} = c_1 \quad (c_1 = c\sqrt{2g}).$$

Hence, using those properties of a cycloid that we have deduced above (see formula (3)), we see that *the brachistochrone is an arc of a cycloid.*

19. The Catenary Curve and the Problem of Minimal Surfaces of Revolution

1. The catenary. A heavy homogeneous chain (or non-stretchable string) is held up by its ends and is allowed to hang freely, with no outside forces interfering except gravity; once in a state of equi-

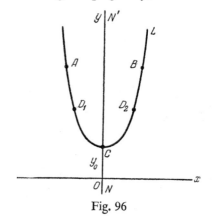

Fig. 96

librium it has the shape of a curve called a *catenary* (Fig. 96). (A homogeneous chain is one whose density ρ is constant; any piece of length h that is cut from the chain will have mass ρh.)

If the chain $\widehat{AB}$ is also fastened at points D_1 and D_2, the equilibrium position of part $\widehat{D_1 D_2}$ of the chain is not changed. Thus the catenary $\overset{\frown}{AB}$ is a continuation of the catenary $\overset{\frown}{D_1D_2}$. So it can be considered that the catenary is continued at both its ends indefinitely, and that the curve $\overset{\frown}{AB}$ is part of an *infinite catenary*.

The point C of the catenary which has the lowest position is called the *vertex*. An infinite catenary is symmetric about the vertical axis NN' which passes through its vertex. Let us take the axis NN' as the y-axis.

Let us consider the right-hand part CL of the catenary. Denote the y-coordinate of some point D of the catenary by y (Fig. 97), the angle between the tangent at this point and the x-axis by α, the length of the arc $\overset{\frown}{CD}$ of the catenary by s.

Let us fasten the points C and D of the catenary to a support. The force which acts on point D is called the *tension P* of the chain at point D and is directed along the tangent to the catenary at point D (Fig. 97). The force P_0 acting at the point C is directed along the

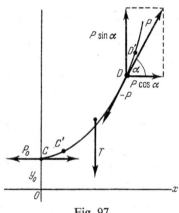

Fig. 97

tangent to the catenary at this point, that is, is parallel to the x-axis (and hence is directed towards the left).

The resultant T of the force of gravity acting on the part $\overset{\frown}{CD}$ of the chain is directed downward parallel to the y-axis; if the piece of chain $\overset{\frown}{CD}$ has length s, then its mass is ρs. Hence the magnitude of T is

$$T = g\rho s, \tag{1}$$

where g is the gravitational constant. The force P has a vertical component directed upward and of magnitude

$$P \sin \alpha,$$

and a horizontal component directed toward the right and having magnitude

$$P \cos \alpha.$$

If the catenary is stationary, then it remains in equilibrium. The horizontal forces P_0 and $P \cos \alpha$, and the vertical forces T and $P \sin \alpha$ acting on the catenary, have opposite directions and cancel each other. Hence, by virtue of (1) we have

$$P \sin \alpha = g\rho s, \tag{2}$$

$$P \cos \alpha = P_0. \tag{3}$$

Now let the chain be displaced along our catenary so that each of its points describes a small arc h of the catenary. Then the chain will assume the position $\overset{\frown}{C'D'}$. Let us find the work done during such a displacement of the chain.

The work done by the force P applied to the point D is Ph; the work done by the force P_0 at point D is $-P_0h$. Thus the total work expended on the displacement of the chain equals

$$R = (P - P_0)h. \tag{4}$$

The chain in the original position $\overset{\frown}{CD}$ consisted of the part $\overset{\frown}{C'D}$ and the small extra part $\overset{\frown}{CC'}$. The chain in the new position $\overset{\frown}{C'D'}$ consists of the same part $\overset{\frown}{C'D}$ and an extra part $\overset{\frown}{DD'}$. Both the extra parts $\overset{\frown}{CC'}$ and $\overset{\frown}{DD'}$ have the same length h and mass ρh, but $\overset{\frown}{CC'}$ has the vertical coordinate y_0 and $\overset{\frown}{DD'}$ has the vertical coordinate y. The result of the work expended is that, in exchange for the additional part $\overset{\frown}{CC'}$ with the coordinate y_0, there has appeared the part $\overset{\frown}{DD'}$ with the same mass and with the coordinate y. Hence we see that the work done is

$$R = g\rho h(y - y_0). \tag{5}$$

From (4) and (5) it follows that

$$P - P_0 = g\rho(y - y_0)$$

or
$$P - g\rho y = P_0 - g\rho y_0. \tag{6}$$

If the chain is moved parallel to itself along the y-axis, then neither its form nor the tension P at its various points is altered. We shall move the catenary in the direction of the y-axis so that the y-coordinate y_0 of its vertex becomes

$$y_0 = \frac{1}{g\rho} P_0. \tag{7}$$

This position of the catenary is called the *standard* position. Below we shall give a geometrical determination of the standard position of a catenary.

With the catenary in standard position, equation (6) takes the simpler form

$$P - \rho g y = 0$$

or

$$y = \frac{1}{\rho g} P. \tag{8}$$

The tension at a point of a catenary in the standard position is proportional to its y-coordinate.

From (3) it follows that

$$\frac{1}{\rho g} P \cos \alpha = \frac{1}{\rho g} P_0$$

or, if equalities (7) and (8) are used,

$$y \cos \alpha = y_0. \tag{9}$$

Equation (9) relates the y-coordinate of a point on a catenary to the angle α between the tangent at this point and the x-axis.

Comparing equation (9) with the equation for the refraction curve (see equation (3), Section 17), we obtain the following:

The path of a ray of light in a medium in which the velocity of light v is inversely proportional to the ordinate y:

$$v = \frac{c}{y}$$

is a catenary in standard position.

2. Geometric determination of the standard position of a catenary. From equalities (2) and (8) it follows that

$$s = \frac{1}{\rho g} P \sin \alpha = y \sin \alpha.$$

Hence

$$y - s = y(1 - \sin \alpha).$$

Finally, by virtue of (9), we obtain

$$y - s = y_0 \frac{1 - \sin \alpha}{\cos \alpha}.$$

Let $\beta = \frac{1}{2}\pi - \alpha$ (β is then the angle between the y-axis and the tangent to the catenary). We obtain

$$y - s = y_0 \frac{1 - \cos \beta}{\sin \beta} = y_0 \frac{2 \sin^2 \frac{1}{2}\beta}{2 \sin \frac{1}{2}\beta \cos \frac{1}{2}\beta} = y_0 \tan \frac{\beta}{2}. \quad (10)$$

Let us consider a segment DE, parallel to the y-axis, directed downward, and of length equal to s (the length of the arc $\overset{\frown}{CD}$ of the catenary) (Fig. 98). If the point D of the arc $\overset{\frown}{CD}$ is held stationary

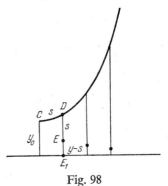

Fig. 98

and point C left free, then under the force of gravity the arc $\overset{\frown}{CD}$ will assume a new position of equilibrium—the vertical segment DE. In short, we say that the arc $\overset{\frown}{CD}$ of the chain "falls" into the position DE. The segment EE_1 of the vertical line, equal to $y - s$, shows how far the end E of the "fallen" part of the chain is from the x-axis.

From formula (9) it follows that

$$\sin \beta = \cos \alpha = \frac{y_0}{y}. \quad (11)$$

Let the point D move without limit upward along the catenary. Its y-coordinate will tend to infinity:

$$y \to \infty.$$

And then, by virtue of (11), sin β approaches zero. But then $\beta \to 0$ also, that is, the angle β between the tangent at point D and the y-axis tends to zero. Then $\tan \frac{1}{2}\beta \to 0$, and, by virtue of (10),

$$\lim_{y \to \infty} (y - s) = 0.$$

The distance from the end E of the fallen arc $\overset{\frown}{CD}$ to the x-axis approaches zero when the end D of this arc tends to infinity.

The x-axis for the standard position of a catenary is that horizontal line which the end E of the fallen arc DE approaches as the end D moves to infinity. The path of the point E is called a trachoid. This characterizes the standard position of a catenary.

3. The minimal surface of revolution. Let us solve the following problem:

Among all the plane curves q which join two given points A and B find that one which, upon revolution around the x-axis, will generate the minimal surface of revolution, that is, the surface of revolution with the least area (Fig. 99).

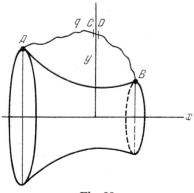

Fig. 99

Let us denote by $V(q)$ the area of the surface of revolution formed by revolving the curve q around the x-axis, and by $T(q)$ the optical length of the curve q in a medium in which the velocity of light v is given by the formula

$$v = \frac{1}{2\pi y}. \tag{12}$$

95

We shall prove that

$$V(q) \quad \text{and} \quad T(q)$$

are equal.

Let $\overset{\frown}{CD}$ be a small arc of length h of the curve q. We shall prove that

$$V(\overset{\frown}{CD}) = T(\overset{\frown}{CD}). \tag{13}$$

Taking $\overset{\frown}{CD}$ to be a small straight line segment and denoting by y the ordinate of the center of gravity of $\overset{\frown}{CD}$, we see that the area of the surface of revolution $V(\overset{\frown}{CD})$ equals the area of the surface of a truncated cone with generators of length h and with a radius of y at the circular midsection. Hence

$$V(\overset{\frown}{CD}) = 2\pi y h.$$

On the other hand, if the velocity of light v at the midpoint of this small segment (and hence approximately for the whole of this segment, as well) equals $1/(2\pi y)$, then its optical length $T(\overset{\frown}{CD})$ equals

$$T(\overset{\frown}{CD}) = \frac{h}{1/(2\pi y)} = 2\pi y h,$$

that is, we arrive at equation (13).

From the numerical equality of the optical length T and the area of the surface of revolution V around the axis for small arcs of the curve q follows their equality for the whole of the curve q. Therefore, if $V(q)$ has its least value for the curve q_0, then the optical length $T(q)$ will have its least value for this same curve. By virtue of Fermat's principle, the curve q_0 is the path of a light ray in our optical medium which joins the points A and B. But in our optical medium the path of a ray of light is a catenary (in standard position).

Thus *among all the curves q which join the points A and B, the catenary $\overset{\frown}{AB}$ (in standard position) generates the minimal surface of revolution $V(q)$ around the x-axis.*

4. Minimal surfaces. As we solved the problem of shortest lines joining given points, so we can pose the question of the least area spanned by a given curve (having a given curve for its boundary)—the so-called *minimal surface*. If the curve r is a plane curve, then the part of the plane Q which is enclosed by it will be the minimal surface spanned by the curve r. If the curve r is not a plane curve, then the minimal surface does not lie in a plane. For example, if we rotate two points A and B about the x-axis, we generate two circles r_1 and r_2 which lie in planes perpendicular to this axis and have their centers on it. Then we have seen that the minimal surface spanned by the circles r_1 and r_2 is the surface obtained by rotating a catenary K (where K passes through A and B, and is in standard position with respect to the given x-axis) about the x-axis.

5. The isoperimetric problem of the minimal surface of revolution. Let us solve a more complicated problem: *among all the curves of a given length l_0 joining points A and B, find that one which, upon revolution around a given axis, generates the minimal surface.* Let us take the axis of revolution LL_1 to be horizontal (Fig. 100). Let us

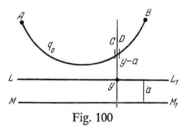

Fig. 100

join the points A and B by a chain of the given length l_0. It will take the form of a catenary $\overparen{AB}$ of the given length l_0. For the x-axis, we take the horizontal straight line MM_1 (parallel to the axis of revolution LL_1), such that relative to it the catenary $\overparen{AB}$ is in standard position.

Let us denote by $V_1(q)$ the area of the surface obtained by revolving a curve q around the x-axis (axis MM_1), by $V(q)$ that obtained by revolving the curve q around the axis LL_1; $l(q)$ denotes the length of the curve q. If a is the distance from the axis LL_1 to the axis MM_1, taken positively if MM_1 lies below LL_1, and otherwise negatively, then

$$V(q) = V_1(q) - 2\pi a l(q). \tag{14}$$

In fact, let $\overparen{CD}$ be a small part of the curve q of length h. If y is the distance from the midpoint of $\overparen{CD}$ to the axis MM_1, then $y - a$ is its distance from the axis LL_1. The length $l(\overparen{CD}) = h$. Further,

$$V_1(CD) = 2\pi h y \quad \text{and} \quad V(CD) = 2\pi h(y - a).$$

97

Since $$2\pi h(y - a) = 2\pi hy - 2\pi ah,$$

we have $$V(\widehat{CD}) = V_1(\widehat{CD}) - 2\pi al(\widehat{CD}). \qquad (15)$$

Thus, formula (14) is true for any small part of curve q. Hence, it is true for the whole curve q.

We are interested in those curves $\bar{q}$ joining A and B whose lengths are $l_0(l(\bar{q}) = l_0)$. For these curves

$$V(\bar{q}) = V_1(\bar{q}) - 2\pi l_0 a,$$

that is, for them, the functions $V(\bar{q})$ and $V_1(\bar{q})$ differ by a constant value $2\pi l_0 a$. These two therefore both assume their minimum for one and the same curve. The catenary q_0 placed in standard position relative to the x-axis gives the minimal value of $V_1(q)$ from among all the curves which join the points A and B, in particular, from among the curves $\bar{q}$ of length l_0.

Hence *this same catenary q_0 gives the minimal value $V(\bar{q})$ for all the curves $\bar{q}$ of length l_0 which join A and B.*

This same property of a catenary can be proved in a different way. Let us consider the collection of all the curves $\bar{q}$ which join the points A and B and which have a given length. Consider each such line as the position of a heavy homogeneous chain of density ρ. Denote the potential energy of the heavy chain in position $\bar{q}$ by $U(\bar{q})$. The minimal value of $U(\bar{q})$ is obtained for the catenary $\bar{q} = q_0$.

In fact, by virtue of Dirichlet's principle (see Section 13), the curve q_0 for which $U(\bar{q})$ has its least value is the equilibrium position of the chain, that is, q_0 is a catenary.

For the x-axis take the horizontal straight line MM_1, and assume that the density ρ of the chain equals 2π. Let us take this straight line as the straight line on which $U = 0$. If y is the vertical coordinate of the midpoint of a small piece $\widehat{CD}$ of the chain of length h (Fig. 100), then

$$U(\widehat{CD}) = \rho hy = 2\pi hy.$$

At the same time, the area of the surface $V(\widehat{CD})$ of revolution of this same small arc $\widehat{CD}$ around the axis MM_1 (the x-axis) equals

$$V(\widehat{CD}) = 2\pi hy.$$

Hence it follows that

$$U(\widehat{CD}) = V(\widehat{CD}),$$

and we obtain the equality

$$U(q) = V(q).$$

For since the values of both the magnitudes U and V are equal for any small part of the curve q, they are equal for the whole curve. Therefore, the catenary, which gives the minimal value of the magnitude $U(\bar{q})$ among all the curves $\bar{q}$ of a given l joining the points A and B, also gives the minimal value of the area $V(\bar{q})$ for such curves.

A magnitude which depends on a curve is called a functional. Thus, for example, the magnitudes $l(q)$, $V(q)$, $T(q)$, $U(q)$, and so on are functionals. Jacques Bernoulli was the first to consider the following problem:

Among the curves of some given length, find that one for which a specified functional $J(q)$ attains its greatest or least value. He called such problems *isoperimetric* problems. The particular case of this problem which we examined in Section 15 is sometimes called the *isoperimetric problem in the restricted sense.* Another example of an isoperimetric problem will now be considered.

20. Connection between Mechanics and Optics

Let us consider the motion of a point in some plane field (in a medium where forces are acting), in which the mechanical law of conservation of energy is applicable:

$$U + T = c, \tag{1}$$

where $U = U(x, y)$ is the potential energy of the moving point, T its kinetic energy, and c the total energy content of the entire system (remaining constant for the duration of the motion). Assuming that the point has unit mass, we have

$$T = \frac{w^2}{2},$$

where w is the velocity of the point. From this and from (1) it follows that

$$w = \sqrt{2T} = \sqrt{[2(c - U)]} = \sqrt{\{2[c - U(x, y)]\}}. \tag{2}$$

Let us consider every possible trajectory, that is, path described by the point, with a given value of total energy c. From formula (2) it is seen that w, the velocity of the moving point, is completely determined by its coordinates x and y, that is, by its position in space.

For example, for motion in a gravitational field, $U = gy$, where g is the gravitational constant and y is the coordinate directed vertically upward; from formula (2) follows

$$w = \sqrt{[2(c - gy)]} = \sqrt{(c_1 - c_2 y)} \quad (c_1 = 2c, \ c_2 = 2g). \quad (3)$$

Let us also consider an optical medium in which the velocity of light v has a value which is the inverse of the mechanical velocity w:

$$v = v(x, y) = \frac{1}{w(x, y)}. \quad (4)$$

Rays of light in a medium with a velocity $v = 1/w$ coincide with the trajectories of the mechanical motion of a point having a velocity $w = w(x, y)$. This constitutes the analogy between mechanics and

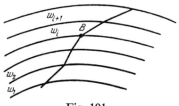

Fig. 101

optics which was established by Hamilton. We know, for example, that in a gravitational field in which the velocity of a point is given by formula (3), the trajectories are parabolas; therefore, in an optical medium in which the velocity of light is $v = 1/\sqrt{(c_1 - c_2 y)}$, the paths of light rays are also parabolas. We know that the paths of light rays in a medium in which the velocities of light are proportional to y, $1/y$, $\sqrt{y}$ are, respectively, semicircles with their centers on the x-axis, catenaries, and cycloids. These lines are also the trajectories of the mechanical motion of points with velocities proportional to $1/y$, y, and $1/\sqrt{y}$, respectively.

To justify this proposition, let us note first of all that forces in a field are directed along normals to the equipotential lines, that is, to lines which have equal values of potential

$$(U(x, y) = \text{const.}),$$

and are directed toward the smaller values of potential (by virtue of (2) the velocity $w = w(x, y)$ is also constant along such lines). Let us draw a system of equipotential lines which are close together.

On each such line the velocity w is constant and changes continuously, the strip between two lines. In Fig. 101 the lines on which in the velocity equals w_1, w_2, . . ., w_i, w_{i+1}, respectively, are marked w_1 w_2, . . ., w_i, w_{i+1}.

Let us now replace our motion by another. In the strip between the lines marked w_i and w_{i+1} let a constant velocity w_i be maintained, which upon the transition through the line marked w_{i+1} changes by a jump. We distort the distribution of velocities, but the closer together the dividing lines (the narrower the strips), the smaller the jumps in the velocities, and the closer the discontinuous distribution

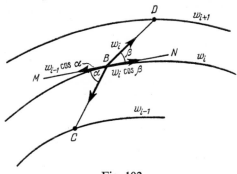

Fig. 102

of velocities comes to the original continuous distribution; the latter can be considered as the limit of the discontinuous distributions as the width of the strips approaches zero.

With a discontinuous distribution of velocities, instead of continuously acting forces (normal to the lines $w =$ const.), impulses of force act normal to the dividing lines, giving rise to the jumps in velocity.

Within the strips there are no forces operating and motion is rectilinear. The trajectories are broken lines with vertices on the dividing lines. Let us consider a part CBD of such a trajectory (Fig. 102). On the segment CB the velocity equals w_{i-1} and is directed along this segment. At the point B let us draw the tangent MN to the dividing curve and denote by α and β the angles of the segments CB and BD with this tangent. The tangential component of the velocities at point B up to the bend and after the bend are equal, respectively, to

$$w_{i-1} \cos \alpha \quad \text{and} \quad w_i \cos \beta.$$

101

Since the impulse of force is directed along the normal to the dividing curve at the point B, the tangential components of the velocities do not change, that is,

$$w_{i-1} \cos \alpha = w_i \cos \beta. \tag{5}$$

Equation (5) expresses the law of refraction of the trajectory at the transition across a dividing line.

Let us now consider an optical medium in which the velocity of light is the inverse of the velocity of the mechanical motion: $v = 1/w$. Then, in our adjacent strips I and II, the velocity of light equals, respectively,

$$v_{i-1} = \frac{1}{w_{i-1}}, \; v_i = \frac{1}{w_i}.$$

By virtue of the law of refraction of light, at point B we have

$$\frac{\cos \alpha}{v_{i-1}} = \frac{\cos \beta}{v_i}$$

or
$$w_{i-1} \cos \alpha = w_i \cos \beta.$$

Thus *light rays in our optical medium are refracted in the same way as the trajectories in a mechanical medium*; they are both broken lines refracted at the same points and in the same way; that is to say, trajectories with velocities w_i in the ith strip coincide with light rays with the velocity of light $v_i = 1/w_i$ in the same strip. We have proved our proposition for discontinuous media.

In the limit, when the widths of the strips approach zero, and when we have a mechanical field with velocities $w = w(x, y)$ and an optical medium with velocities of light $v = v(x, y) = 1/[w(x, y)]$, then the coinciding broken trajectories and light rays become coinciding curved trajectories and light rays.

This connection between optics and mechanics, which was noted by Hamilton, plays a very important role in contemporary physics.

In conclusion let us note that general methods for the solution of problems of finding the maxima and minima of functionals constitute a subject of investigation in the field of mathematics called the *calculus of variations*. The fundamentals of this discipline were developed by the great mathematicians of the eighteenth century, L. Euler and J. Lagrange.